D1649678

Toad of Toad Hall

Toad of Toad Hall

A PLAY FROM
KENNETH GRAHAME'S BOOK
'The Wind in the Willows'

BY

A. A. MILNE

METHUEN & CO LTD
11 *New Fetter Lane, London,* EC4

Hardback edition first published 11 April 1929
Reprinted thirty times
Reprinted 1970
SBN 416 38770 5
21.11

School edition first published 11 April 1929
Reprinted thirty-one times
Reprinted 1970
SBN 423 75220 0
20.12

Paperback edition first published 1970
SBN 416 07790 0

Printed and bound in Great Britain by Butler & Tanner Ltd, Frome and London

INTRODUCTION

THERE are familiarities which we will allow only ourselves to take. Your hands and my hands are no cleaner than anybody else's hands, yet the sort of well-thumbed bread-and-butter which we prefer is that on which we have placed our own thumbs. It may be that to turn Mr. Kenneth Grahame into a play is to leave unattractive finger-marks all over him, but I love his books so much that I cannot bear to think of anybody else disfiguring them. That is why I accepted a suggestion, which I should have refused in the case of any other book as too difficult for me, that I should dramatize *The Wind in the Willows*.

There are two well-known ways in which to make a play out of a book. You may insist on being faithful to the author, which means that the scene in the aeroplane on page 673 must be got in somehow, however impossible dramatically, or, with somebody else's idea in your pocket, you may insist on being faithful to yourself, which means that by the middle of Act III everybody will realize how right the original author was to have made a book of it. There may be a third way, in which case I have tried to follow it. If, as is more likely, there isn't, then I have *not* made a play of *The Wind in the Willows*. But I have, I hope, made some sort of entertainment, with enough of Kenneth Grahame in it to appease his many admirers, and enough of me in it to justify my name upon the title-page.

Of course I have left out all the best parts of the

book; and for that, if he has any knowledge of the theatre, Mr. Grahame will thank me. With a Rat and Mole from the Green Room Club, a Baby Otter from Conti, a Pan from Clarkson's, and a wind (off) whispering in the reeds of Harker, we are not going to add any fresh thrill to the thrill which the loveliness of *The Piper at the Gates of Dawn* has already given its readers. Whether there is, indeed, any way of putting these animals on the stage must be left to managers, professional and amateur, to find out. But it seemed clear to me that Rat and Toad, Mole and Badger could only face the footlights with hope of success if they were content to amuse their audiences. There are both beauty and comedy in the book, but the beauty must be left to blossom there, for I, anyhow, shall not attempt to transplant it.

But can one transplant even the comedy ? Perhaps it has happened to you, as it has certainly happened to me, that you have tried to explain a fantastic idea to an entirely matter-of-fact person. ' But they *don't*,' he says, and ' You *can't*,' and ' I don't see *why*, just because——' and ' Even if you assume that——' and ' I thought you said just now that he *hadn't*.' By this time you have thrown the ink-pot at him, with enough of accuracy, let us hope, to save you from his ultimatum, which is this : ' However fantastic your assumption, you *must* work it out logically '—that is to say, realistically.

To such a mind *The Wind in the Willows* makes no appeal, for it is not worked out logically. In reading the book, it is necessary to think of Mole, for instance, sometimes as an actual mole, sometimes as such a mole in human clothes, sometimes as a mole grown to human size, sometimes as walking on two legs, sometimes on four. He is a mole, he isn't a mole. What is he? I don't know. And, not being a matter-of-fact person, I don't mind. At least, I do know, and still I don't mind. He is a fairy, like so many immortal characters in fiction ; and, as a fairy, he can do, or be, anything.

But the stage has no place for fairies. There is a horrid realism about the theatre, from which, however hard we try, we can never quite escape. Once we put Mole and his friends on the boards we have to be definite about them. What do they look like?

To answer this here is difficult. To say at rehearsal what they do not look like will be easy. Vaguely I see them made up on the lines of the Cat in *The Blue Bird* and the Hen Pheasant in *Chantecler*. As regards their relative sizes, Toad should be short and fat, Badger tall and elderly, Rat and Mole young and slender. Indeed Mole might well be played by some boyish young actress. The ' humans ', Judge, Policeman, Usher and the rest, should be as fantastic as possible, with a hint of the animal world about them. Only Phoebe must keep her own pretty face, but even she must be no mortal. I see her in a ballet skirt or something entirely unsuitable to a jailer's daughter, pirouetting absurdly about the prison.

But no doubt the producer will see them all differently. If he is an amateur, I shall congratulate him on his enterprise and wish him luck ; if he is a professional, I shall be there to watch him, and, no doubt, to tell him enthusiastically how much better his ideas are than mine.

A. A. M.

Toad of Toad Hall

CHARACTERS

Nurse	Policeman
Marigold	Judge
The Mole	Phoebe
The Water-Rat	Washerwoman
Mr. Badger	Mama Rabbit
Toad	Harold Rabbit
Alfred	Lucy Rabbit
Chief Weasel	Fox
Chief Stoat	Barge-Woman
Chief Ferret	A Brave Young Weasel
First Field-Mouse	(Henry)
Second Field-Mouse	A Foolish Ferret
Usher	(James)

Barge-horse, Squirrels, Rabbits, Ferrets, Weasels, Stoats, Field-mice, Turkey, Duck, Back Legs of Alfred, etc., etc.

SCENES

PROLOGUE AND ACT I

Down by the Willows

ACT II

ACT III

ACT IV

EPILOGUE

The Wind in the Willows

TOAD OF TOAD HALL

ACT I

Down by the Willows

SCENE.—*The River Bank. A warm morning in Spring. NURSE was knitting a sock, but seems to have fallen asleep over it. This leaves MARIGOLD (who is twelve) to amuse herself. She is lying on her front, and talking down the telephone. At least she has the trumpet of one daffodil to her ear, and of another to her mouth, and has apparently just got on to the Exchange.*

MARIGOLD. Hallo, is that the Exchange ? I want River Bank 1001. . . . Hallo, is that the Water Rat's house ? . . . Oh, I *beg* your pardon. They've given me the wrong number. . . . Oh, Exchange, you've given me the wrong number. I wanted Mr. Rat's house and you've given me Mr. Badger's. (*To herself*) Sorry you've been tr-r-roubled. . . . Hallo, is that the Water Rat's house ? Is that Mr. Rat speaking ? Good morning, Mr. Rat, this is Marigold speaking. . . . Yes, isn't it a delightful day ? . . . Yes. Well, almost alone. Nurse is here, but she's asleep. How's Mr. Mole ? . . . Oh, haven't you seen him ? I expect he's very busy spring-cleaning. You see, when your house is *all* basement, there's such a lot of spring-cleaning to be done. . . . Yes, I prefer a river-side residence too. . . . May I really come one day ? How lovely. . . . No, not to-morrow, I'm having tea with Mr. Toad. . . . Yes, conceited, but *so* nice. . . . I saw Mr. Otter just now, just before I rang you up. . . . No, I don't know him very well, but I think he's sweet. . . . Will you really ? And if Mr. Mole——

NURSE (*who was not asleep*). Well, I declare, Miss Marigold, you do think of funny things.

MARIGOLD (*hurriedly*). Oh, Nurse is awake. Good-bye. (*She puts down the telephone and says sternly*) Have you been overhearing, Nurse ?

NURSE (*nodding*). And wondering at you, dearie. Who ever heard the like ?

MARIGOLD. It's very bad manners to overhear a perfectly private telephone conversation.

NURSE. Couldn't help it, dearie, you're that funny —with your Mr. Rat and Mr. Toad and all, just as if they were yooman beings——

MARIGOLD. Well, but so they are.

NURSE (*surprised at this*). Yooman beings ?

MARIGOLD. Yes. I mean they are as human to themselves as—as we are to us.

NURSE (*after a gallant effort*). No, it's no good, dearie, I can't follow it.

MARIGOLD. I mean, they must *seem* quite big and grown up and human to each other, and if we lived in their world, then they would seem big and grown up to us, just like real people.

NURSE. Now, fancy that !

MARIGOLD. Mr. Toad, he's all puffed out and conceited, but very nice, you know, and very sorry afterwards for talking so much about himself. And

Mr. Rat's a dear—that's him I was talking to just now. He's very quick and clever and helpful, and his little sharp eyes are always looking out so as to see that he doesn't hurt people's feelings. And Mr. Mole—I'm not sure about *him*. You see, he lives underground a good deal, and doesn't go out into society much, so I should think he'd be rather simple, and not liking to talk about himself, and just saying ' Yes ' and ' No ', and waiting to be asked before he has a second cup. And then Mr. Badger—of course he's grey, and much older than the others, and very fatherly—and sleeps a good deal with a handkerchief over his face, and says ' Now, now, now ' and ' Well, well well ' when he's woken up. And Mr. Otter——

NURSE. Well, well, well, fancy that now ! Why, you might almost have seen them at it, the way you talk.

MARIGOLD. I have.

NURSE. Never !

MARIGOLD. Yes. One morning. I came out here early, oh, ever so early. Nobody was up—you weren't up, and the birds weren't up, and even the sun wasn't up—and everything was so still that there was no sound in all the world, except just the wind in the willows, whispering ever so gently.

NURSE (*professionally*). What your poor mother would have said—— (*Eagerly*) Well, and what happened ?

MARIGOLD. I don't know. I sat there and waited for everything to wake up, and then by and by I heard something—music, very thin and clear and far off—and then—well, then there was the sun, and it was daylight, and it seemed as if I had just woken up myself. But it was all different. Something had happened. I didn't know what, but I seemed to understand more than I did before—to have been *with* them.

NURSE. Mr. Toad and Mr. Mole and all them ?

MARIGOLD. Yes. I've never really seen them since. I pretend to talk to them, just as if they were really there, but—— (*With sudden excitement*) Wouldn't it be lovely if they suddenly came out and began to talk—Mole from under the ground there, and the Water Rat from his hole in the bank, and the old Badger from the dead leaves in the ditch, and Mr. Toad——

NURSE. I should be that frightened, if they were all big.

MARIGOLD. Oh no, you wouldn't, because they wouldn't know *we* were here. We should just listen to them, without their knowing anything about it. (*She calls out*) Mr. Mole ! Mr. Rat ! Mr. Toad ! Oh, Nurse, wouldn't it be *lovely* ?

NURSE. Oo, I can hear something ! Listen !

MARIGOLD. That's the music again. Quick ! Hide !

[*It is dark suddenly, and we hear music, very thin and clear and far off : ' the horns of Elfland faintly blowing '. Gradually it grows light again. There is no* NURSE, *no* MARIGOLD *now. But near where* MARIGOLD *was lying there is a curious upheaval going on. The earth moves and humps up and falls back again. Somebody is at work underneath. We hear breathings and mutterings. In a little while we can distinguish words. It is our old friend* MOLE.

MOLE (*as he comes laboriously into the daylight*).

Scrape and scratch and scrabble and scrooge—scrooge and scrabble and scrape and scratch—up we go, up we go! . . . Pop! (*He stands up and brushes himself.*) Ah! (*He takes a deep breath of daylight.*) This is fine! This is better than whitewash. Hang spring-cleaning! (*He walks about, making ecstatic noises to himself.*) Oh, what a day! Oh my, oh my, oh my! Blow spring-cleaning! (*He rubs his eyes with his paw.*) Is that a River? Oh my, oh my! *Bother* spring-cleaning!

> [*The river has hollowed out a little bay here, so that* Nurse *and* Marigold, *from where they are sitting in Box B, can see their own side of the bank, where it bends round in a curve, and they can see* Rat's *front door and they can see bright eyes and a sharp friendly face, with whiskers, as the* Water Rat *comes out of it.*

Rat. Hallo, Mole!

Mole. Hallo, Rat!

Rat. Don't seem to have seen you about before.

Mole (*shyly*). I—I don't go out much, as a rule.

Rat (*cheerily*). Prefer home-life? *I* know. Very good thing too in its way.

Mole. Yes, you see, I—— This is a river, isn't it?

Rat. *The* River.

Mole (*simply*). I've never seen a river before.

Rat (*staggered*). Never seen a—— You never—— Well, I—— What *have* you been doing then?

Mole. Is it as nice as that?

Rat. Nice? My dear young friend, believe me, it's the *only* thing. There is *nothing*—absolutely nothing—half so much worth doing as simply messing about by a river. (*Dreamily*) Simply messing—

messing about by a river—or *in* a river—or *on* a river. It doesn't matter which.

MOLE. But what do you *do* ?

RAT. Nothing. Just mess about. That's the charm of it ; you're always busy, and yet you never do anything in particular ; and when you've done it, there's always something else to do, and you can do it if you like, but you'd much better not. . . . And so you've never even *seen* a river before ? Well, well !

MOLE. Never. And you actually live by it. What a jolly life it sounds.

RAT. By it and with it and on it and in it. It's brother and sister to me, and aunts and company, and food and drink, and—naturally—washing. It's my world, and I don't want any other.

MOLE. Isn't it a bit dull at times ? Just you and the river and no one else to pass a word with ?

RAT. No one else to—no one—— Oh well, I mustn't be hard on you. You're new to it. But believe me, my dear young friend, the River Bank is so crowded nowadays that many people are moving away altogether. Otters, kingfishers, dabchicks, moorhens—— No one else to—— Oh, my dear young friend !

MOLE (*timidly*). I am afraid you must think me very ignorant.

RAT (*kindly*). Not at all. Naturally, not being used to it. Look here, what are you doing to-day ?

MOLE (*hesitatingly*). I—I *was* spring-cleaning.

RAT. On a day like this !

MOLE. That's just it. Sometimes I seem to hear a voice within me say ' Whitewash ', and then another voice says ' Hang whitewash ! ' (*Slowly*) And I don't

quite know which of the—— I don't quite know—I
don't qui—— Oh, *hang* whitewash !

RAT (*patting him encouragingly*). That's the spirit.
Well, what I was about to suggest was a trifle of
lunch on the bank here, and then I'd take you round
and introduce you to a few of my friends. Does that
appeal to you at all ?

MOLE (*ecstatically*). Does it appeal to me ? Does
it ? Oh my, oh my, oh my !

RAT (*soothingly*). There, there ! You don't want
to get *too* excited. It's only just a trifle of lunch.
Cold tongue—cold ham—cold chicken—salad—French
rolls — cress sandwiches — hard-boiled eggs — bloater
paste — tinned peaches — meringues — ginger beer —
lemonade — milk — chocolate — oranges—— Nothing
special—only just——

MOLE (*faintly*). Stop, stop ! Oh my, oh my ! Oh
what a day !

RAT. That's all right. You'll feel better soon.
Now just you wait here—don't go falling into the river
or anything like that—and I'll be back in two minutes
with the luncheon-basket.

MOLE (*wiping away the tears*). Oh, Mr. Rat, my
generous friend, I—I—words fail me for the moment—
I — (*he holds out his hand*) — your kindness — that
expression, if I caught it correctly, ' luncheon-basket '
—a comparative stranger like myself—did I hear you
say ' bloater paste ' ?—you—I—— (*He opens his eyes
and finds that* RAT *has gone.*) Oh ! (*He walks over to a
bank of dead leaves and sits down on it.*) Oh, what a day !

>   [*It is indeed a day. For suddenly the leaves
>   begin to move beneath him, and* MOLE *rises and
>   falls with the motion of a small boat on a choppy*

sea. A final upheaval dislodges him altogether, the leaves scatter and disclose the recumbent form of MR. BADGER. *Slowly he humps himself into a sitting position and addresses the astonished* MOLE.

BADGER (*gruffly*). Now the *very* next time this happens I shall be exceedingly angry. I have had to speak about it before, and I don't want to speak about it again. But I will *not* have people sitting down on me just as if I were part of the landscape. Now who is it this time? Speak up!

MOLE. Oh, please, Mr. Badger, it's only me.

BADGER. Well, if it's only you, that makes a difference. I don't want to be hard on you. But I put it to you that when an animal is being particularly busy underneath a few leaves, thinking very deeply about things, giving himself up to very serious reflection, he does *not* want to be disturbed. And it *is* disturbing, my little fellow, to have somebody sitting down carelessly on your person, and stretching his legs in an independent sort of way, and——

RAT (*emerging with the lunch*). Here, Mole, give us a hand with this basket. Hallo! Why, it's Mr. Badger!

BADGER. Ah, Ratty, my dear little man, delighted to see you. I was just telling this little fellow——

RAT. By the way, let me introduce you. My friend, Mr. Mole.

BADGER. Don't mention it. Any friend of yours, Ratty——

MOLE (*timidly*). How do you do, Mr. Badger? I am very proud to meet you. I'm sure I'm extremely sorry——

BADGER. That's all right, that's all right. Any friend of Ratty's may sit down *where* he likes and *when* he likes, or I'll know the reason why. Well, and what are you two little fellows doing ?

RAT. Just having a trifle of lunch. Stay and join us, won't you ?

MOLE (*shyly*). Oh do, Mr. Badger ! It's a picnic !

[*He helps* RAT *up with the basket.*

BADGER. H'm ! Picnics aren't much in my line. Got company coming ?

RAT. Only Mole and myself. Unless Toad happens along.

MOLE (*in an ecstatic whisper*). There's cold tongue— cold chicken—salad—French rolls—cress sandwiches— hard-boiled eggs——

BADGER. Well, if you're sure there's no company. You know, Ratty, I never did like society.

[*He sits down heavily on the basket, much to*
  MOLE'S *disappointment, who was hoping to get*
  to work at once.

RAT. Can't say I see much in it myself.

BADGER. Sensible animal. And what about your friend Mr. Mole ?

MOLE. Oh, I live a *very* quiet life, Mr. Badger. A field-mouse or two drops in from time to time—perhaps half a dozen of them will come carol-singing at Christmas—but beyond that I hardly see anybody.

BADGER. That's right. Ratty, your little friend promises well.

RAT. Yes, but you're sitting on the lunch, and we can't——

BADGER (*taking no notice*). He has the right ideas.

(*Solemnly*) How different from *one* whom we could mention !

RAT. Oh, Toad ? Toady's all right.

BADGER (*shaking his head sadly*). Ah me !

MOLE. I have heard of the great Mr. Toad. He's very rich, isn't he ?

RAT. Richest animal in these parts, and got one of the nicest houses, though we don't admit as much to Toady. Tudor residence—mullioned windows—bath, hot and cold—and every modern convenience, including carriage sweep. Entertains a lot. Always glad to see you night *or* day. A good fellow, Toady.

BADGER. Ah me !

MOLE. He must indeed be a very nice animal.

RAT. So simple, so good-natured, so affectionate. Perhaps he's not very clever—we can't all be geniuses ; and it may be that he is both boastful and conceited. But he has some great qualities has Toady.

MOLE. It would be a privilege to make his acquaintance.

RAT. Oh, you'll see him all right. He's sure to be along soon.

BADGER. And when you see him, my little friend, take warning by him. Society has been his undoing.

RAT. Well, I wouldn't say that. I——

BADGER. If it were not for the desire to shine before his acquaintances, what a much more dependable animal Toad would be ! I knew his father. I knew his grandfather. I knew his uncle, the Archdeacon—— Ah me !

RAT. Cheer up, old Badger. We'll take him in hand one day and make a better animal of him.

BADGER. Indeed we must. It is a duty I owe to

his father.   And now that the year is really beginning, and the nights are shorter, and half-way through them one rouses and feels fidgety, and wanting to be up and doing by sunrise, if not before—*you* know——

RAT. *I* know.

BADGER. Well, then, *now* we—you and me and our friend the Mole here, we'll take him in hand and *make* a better animal of him.   That is, if we have any more of his nonsense.

RAT (*nodding*). That's right, Badger.   But he's a good fellow, Toady.   Doesn't *mean* any harm, you know.   Just his way.

MOLE. What *is* his way ?

BADGER. You tell him, Rat.

RAT. Crazes.   He always has crazes.   First it's for sailing, and then it's for punting, and then it's for astronomy, and then it's for carriage horses ; and whatever it is, he always has *the* most expensive, and lots of 'em, and knows all about it, or thinks he does, and—— Just get up a moment, Badger, you're sitting on the basket.

BADGER (*not moving*). I knew his father.   I knew his uncle the——

RAT. Whatever it is, he must have the best.   And then in a week, he's forgotten about it, and started something else.

BADGER. Society.   That's what's undone him. The craving to shine.   (*Solemnly to* MOLE) Very sad, my young friend, very sad.   I knew his grandfather.

MOLE (*helpfully*). Dear, dear !

BADGER.   What his poor father would have said——

TOAD (*off*). Hallo !

RAT (*cheerily*). Hallo, Toady ! (*He waves a paw.*)

I thought he'd come along soon. You see, he *likes* company.

BADGER (*sadly*). Ah me !

  [TOAD *comes in boisterously, as full of himself as usual.*

TOAD. Hallo, you fellows ! This is splendid ! Hallo, old Badger ! Dear old Ratty ! (*He shakes him warmly by the paw.*) Hallo ! (*He seizes* MOLE'S *paw and works it up and down.*) And dear old Badger ! (*He passes on to* BADGER) How *are* you ?

BADGER. So-so.

TOAD. Splendid, splendid !

RAT. My friend, Mr. Mole.

TOAD (*going back enthusiastically to* MOLE). *How* are you ? (*He shakes his paw vigorously.*) Splendid, eh ? That's good. And old Ratty. *And* Badger.

BADGER. We were talking about you, my young friend.

TOAD (*spreading himself with delight*). Ah well, the penalty of fame. Eh, Ratty ? One gets talked about. One is discussed. One is a topic of conversation. One is speculated about. There it is. One can't help it. Well, Ratty, old man, and how are you ?

RAT. *I'm* all right. We were just going to have a trifle of lunch. You'd better join us. (*Pulling at the basket again.*) I say, Badger, old man——

TOAD. No, no, you all come up to *my* house. Come up to Toad Hall. *I'll* give you lunch, the finest lunch you ever had.

MOLE (*unable to imagine anything superior to* RAT'S *effort*). But there's cold tongue — cold ham — cold chicken—salad—French rolls—cress sandwiches—hard-boiled——

Toad. Pooh ! Wait till you've seen mine. Ratty knows. Eh, Ratty ? They're quite famous—been referred to in books. ' Another select little luncheon-party at Toad Hall.' That sort of thing.

Mole (*awed*). Oh !

> [*He looks anxiously at* Rat, *to whom, after all, he is engaged for lunch.*

Rat. Now, now, Toad !

Badger. Well, I'll be moving.   [*He rises slowly.*

Rat (*getting to the basket at last*). Thanks, old chap.

Toad. That's right. We'll all be moving. (*To* Mole) It's only a step to Toad Hall. Jacobean residence—with bits of Tudor. Finest house on the river. You'll like it.

Mole (*eagerly*). I'm sure I shall.

Badger (*to* Mole). Good-bye, my young friend. We shall meet again. And before very long, if I'm not mistaken. Good-bye, Ratty.

Rat. Sure you won't stay to lunch.

Toad. But you are coming to lunch with *me*, old Badger.

Badger (*severely*). Nobody is coming to lunch with you, Toad. Many a time I have lunched at Toad Hall with your father ; an animal of few words, but of what an intellect ! Ah me ! How different from—but I will not go into that now. Hour after hour, when lunch was cleared away, we would sit there meditating. I knew your grandfather, worthy animal that he was. Many a time have I lunched with him at Toad Hall. Little did he think, as we sat there reflecting, that one day—but I shall refer to that later. Good-bye, my unhappy young friend.   [*He goes out heavily.*

MOLE (*anxiously*). Isn't Mr. Badger feeling very well?

TOAD (*recovering himself*). Poor old Badger, he gets that way sometimes. No fire, no spirit, no—what's the word—*élan*. Well, well, we can't all have it. Hallo, Ratty, where are you off to?

RAT (*going for it*). The corkscrew.

TOAD (*not moving*). Now, let *me* fetch it. (*To* MOLE) Tell you what, you must come and stay with me. Let me put you up at Toad Hall.

MOLE. It's very kind of you, but——

TOAD. That's all right. Plenty of room at Toad Hall. Open house for my friends. Always glad to see them. Now what have we got for lunch? (*He assumes the position of host.*) Try one of these sandwiches. (*As* RAT *emerges with the corkscrew.*) Come along, Ratty, try one of these sandwiches. Got the corkscrew? Good. (*To* MOLE) Let me open you one of these bottles. Sit down, Ratty; make yourself comfortable.

RAT (*quietly to* MOLE). Got everything you want?

MOLE. Yes, thank you.

RAT. That's right. Well, Toady, and what have you been doing lately? Boating? Haven't seen you on the river this last day or two.

TOAD. The river! Boating! Bah! Silly boyish amusement. I've given that up *long* ago. Sheer waste of time. No, I've discovered the real thing, the only genuine occupation. I propose to devote the remainder of my life to it. To think of the wasted years that lie behind me, squandered in trivialities!

RAT. What's that? Help yourself, Mole.

TOAD. Aha, what is it? Come to Toad Hall and you shall see.

MOLE. Oh, do let's.

RAT. All right, we'll drop in one afternoon.

TOAD. Drop in ? One afternoon ? Nonsense ! You're coming to stay. Always welcome, that's my motto. I've had it picked out in green on the front-door mat. ' Always welcome. A home from home.' (*To* MOLE) You'd like to come, wouldn't you ?

RAT. Sorry, but Mole is staying with *me*.

TOAD. Now, you dear good old Ratty, don't begin talking in that stiff and sniffy sort of way, because you know you've got to come. And don't argue ; it's the one thing I can't stand. You surely don't mean to stick to your dull fusty old river all your life and just live in a hole in the bank ? Come and stay with me, and I'll show you the world.

RAT. I don't *want* to see the world. And I *am* going to stick to my old river, *and* live in a hole, just as I've always done. And I'm going to teach Mole all about the river, aren't I, Mole ? And Mole is going to stick to me and do as I do, aren't you, Mole ?

MOLE (*loyally*). Of course I am. I'll always stick to you, Rat. (*Wistfully*) All the same, it sounds as though it might have been—well, rather fun at Toad Hall.

TOAD. Fun ? Wait till you see what I've got. I've got the finest—— Well, wait till you see it. Pass the sandwiches, Mole, there's a good fellow. (*To* RAT) Seen any of the Wild-Wooders lately ?

RAT. No.

MOLE. Who are the Wild-Wooders ?

RAT (*pointing across the river*). They live over there in the Wild Wood. We don't go there very much, we River-Bankers.

Mole. Aren't they—aren't they very nice people in there ?

Toad. They daren't show their noses round Toad Hall, that they daren't. I'd soon send them packing.

Rat. The squirrels are all right. And the rabbits, of course. And then there's Badger. Dear old Badger. Nobody interferes with *him*. They'd better not.

Toad. And nobody wouldn't interfere with me neither, if I lived there.

Mole. Why, who should ?

Rat. Well, of course there are others. Weasels and stoats and ferrets and so on. They're all right in a way—I'm very good friends with them——

Toad. So am I.

Rat. Pass the time of day when we meet and all that. But they break out sometimes, there's no denying it, and then—well, you really can't trust them, and that's a fact. And if they don't like you, they— well, they show it.

Toad. I wouldn't ask them to Toad Hall, not if they sat up and begged me to. I'm not afraid of them ; I just don't like them. They've got no man- ners, no finesse, if you understand me. Some people are like that, of course. It isn't their fault. You either have finesse, or you haven't. That's how I look at it. Pass the meringues, Mole, there's a good fellow.

> [*But* Mole *is staring beyond* Toad *at something strange which is approaching—a gaily painted caravan drawn by an old grey horse.*

Rat. What is it, Mole ?

MOLE. Whatever's that ?   [*They all turn.*

ALFRED (*the horse*). Oh, there you are. I've been looking for you everywhere.

TOAD (*excitedly*). Now isn't this lucky ? Just at the psycho—psycho—what's the word ?

ALFRED (*hopefully*). Encyclopaedia. That is, if you ask *me*.

TOAD. I didn't ask you. Ratty, *you* know the word——

ALFRED. Introduce me to your friends, won't you ? I do get so frightfully left out of it.

TOAD. My friends Mr. Rat and Mr. Mole. This is Alfred.

ALFRED. Pleased to meet you. If you're coming my way, you must let me take you. Only I do like a little conversation. (*To* TOAD) Encyclopaedia, that was the word you wanted.

RAT (*sadly*). So this is the latest ?

TOAD (*eagerly*). Absolutely the very latest. There isn't a more beautiful one, a more compact one, a more—what's the word ?

ALFRED. Heavy.

TOAD. A more up-to-date one, a more——

RAT. So this is the latest craze ! I understand. Boating is played out. He's tired of it, and done with it.

ALFRED. Don't blame *me*. I wasn't consulted about this at all ; but if I had been, I should have said Boats. Stick to Boats.

TOAD. My dear old Ratty, you don't understand. Boating—well—a pleasant amusement for the young. I say nothing against it. But there's real life for you— (*he waves a paw at the van*)—in that little cart. The

C

open road, the dusty highway, the heath, the common, the hedgerows, the rolling downs !

ALFRED. *And* the ups. However, nobody consults *me*. Nobody minds what *I* think.

TOAD (*warming to it*). Camps, villages, towns, cities ! Here to-day, up and off somewhere else to-morrow ! Travel, change, interest, excitement ! The whole world before you, and a horizon that's always changing.

MOLE (*ecstatically*). Oh my ! Oh my !

TOAD. And mind, this is the very finest cart of the sort that was ever built, without any exception. Come inside and look at the arrangements, Mole. Planned 'em all myself, I did.

MOLE (*timidly to* RAT). We could just look inside, couldn't we ? It wouldn't—wouldn't *mean* anything.

ALFRED (*airily*). Nothing ! Nothing !

RAT (*reluctantly*). Oh well, we may as well look at it, now we *are* here. (*Sadly*) Oh, Toady !

TOAD (*leading the way*). All complete ! You see— biscuits, potted lobster, sardines—everything you can possibly want. Soda-water here—baccy there——

[*He shows them into the van, and then his voice dies away.*

ALFRED (*to anybody who is listening*). That's right. Go inside and enjoy yourselves ! Talk to each other, tell each other little stories, but don't ask *me* to join in the conversation. Encyclopaedia—that was the word he wanted. *I* could have told him.

TOAD (*emerging*). Bacon, jam, cards, dominoes— you'll find that nothing whatever has been forgotten.

ALFRED (*with feeling*). I've noticed it.

TOAD. Well, what do you think of it, Mole ?

MOLE. It's lovely !

TOAD. Glad you like it. What about starting this afternoon ?

RAT (*slowly*). I beg your pardon, did I overhear you say something about ' starting ' ?

ALFRED. Starting—that's what he said. I'm not even consulted.

TOAD. Come on, we'll just put the rest of the lunch inside—come on, Mole, give us a hand——

MOLE (*torn between the two of them*). Oh, Ratty !

TOAD. Come on, Ratty, old fellow. This is the real life for a gentleman. Talk about your old river !

> [*He begins packing up the lunch.*

RAT. I *don't* talk about my river. You *know* I don't, Toad. . . . But I *think* about it. I think about it—all the time.

MOLE (*squeezing* RAT'S *paw*). I'll do whatever you like, Ratty. We won't go. I want to stay with *you*. And—and learn about your river.

RAT. No, no, we'd better see it out now. It wouldn't be safe for him to go off by himself. It won't take long—his crazes never do.

ALFRED. When *I* was young, it was considered bad manners to whisper, and leave people out of conversations. (*In a loud conversational voice*) My own view— since asked—of the climatic conditions, is that the present anticyclonic disturbance in the——

TOAD. Here, give us a hand, Mole. . . . That's right. . . . All aboard ? Here, we're forgetting the corkscrew. Will you get it ? (MOLE *trots back for it.*) Don't bother. *I'll*—— Oh, you've got it. Good ! Now then, are we all ready ?

ALFRED. No.

Toad. You get up there, Mole. (Mole *sits on the shaft on one side of the caravan.*) You on the other side, Ratty ? Or would you rather—— (Rat *goes to the horse's head.*) Oh, are *you* going to lead him ? I will, if you like. Sure you don't mind ? Right, then I'll get up here. Now then, right away ! [*They start off.*

Alfred (*to* Rat). You mark my words. No good will come of this. But don't blame *me*. That's all. Don't blame *me* afterwards. Psychological—that was the word he wanted. Not encyclopaedia. I thought it seemed funny somehow. Psychological.

[*The caravan goes out.*

•   •   •   •   •

> [*It grows dark. A thunderstorm, you would say, is brewing. In the darkness scuffling noises can be heard ; breathings. It becomes lighter, and now we can see. The* Wild-Wooders *are here !* Ferrets, Weasels, Stoats *perform weird evolutions as they chant their terrible war-song :*

Toad ! Toad ! Down with Toad !
Down with the popular, successful Toad !

> [*The three* Chief Conspirators *form a mystic circle in the middle and utter this horrid incantation :*

Chief Ferret :
    O may his bathroom cistern spring a leak !
Chief Weasel :
    On Sunday morning may his collar squeak !
Chief Stoat :
    May all his laces tie themselves in knots,

CHIEF FERRET :
   And may his fountain-pen make frequent blots !
CHIEF WEASEL :
   May he forget to wind his watch at night,
CHIEF STOAT :
   And may his dancing-pumps be *much* too tight !
                    [*They dance solemnly.*
THE FERRETS :
   Every ill which Toad inherits
   Will be welcomed by the Ferrets.
ALL :
   Down with Toad !   Down with Toad !

THE WEASELS :
   Day and night the elder Weasels
   Hope that he will have the measles.
ALL :
   Down with Toad !   Down with Toad !

THE STOATS :
   How the happy little Stoats
   Laugh when he is off his oats !
ALL :
   Down with Toad !   Down with Toad !
   Toad !   Toad !   Down with Toad !
   Down with the popular, successful Toad !

   [*It grows dark again. The* WILD-WOODERS *can
   still be heard chanting their diabolical refrain,
   but they can no longer be seen. There is a loud
   clap of thunder ; it is daylight again ; the*
   WILD-WOODERS *have vanished. Then the
   ' poop-poop ' of a motor-car is heard, followed*

*by a loud crash.   Suddenly in comes a violently-
excited* ALFRED, *the broken ends of the shafts
attached to him, but no caravan.*   MOLE *follows.*

MOLE (*soothingly to* ALFRED). There, there ! . . .
There, there ! (*But* ALFRED *refuses to ' there, there ! '
He careers round the stage, pursued by the conciliatory*
MOLE.) There, there ! It's all right, Alfred. (*Very
reassuringly*) It's all *right*.

[RAT *comes in, supporting a dazed* TOAD.

RAT (*turning and shaking his fist at something*). You
villains ! You scoundrels, you highwaymen, you—
you——

ALFRED (*still gyrating*). Road-hogs. That's the
word. Always come to me if you want the right
word. Road-hogs.

RAT. You road-hogs ! I'll have the law of you !
Rushing about the country at fifty miles an hour ! I'll
write to all the papers about you ! I'll take you
through all the Courts ! (*Turning anxiously to* TOAD)
How are you feeling now, Toady ? Mole, come and
give us a hand with poor old Toad. I'm afraid he's
pretty bad.

MOLE (*catching up* ALFRED *at last*). There, there !
That's all right now, isn't it ? (*Going to* RAT) Poor old
Toad !

[*He takes his other arm, and together he and* RAT
*conduct the dazed one to a grassy bank, and sit
him gently down.*

ALFRED. I said that no good would come of it,
and now you see. A cataclysm—that's what the whole
thing's been.

RAT (*anxiously*). Speak to us, Toady, old man !
How is it ?

TOAD (*staring in front of him with a rapt expression*).
Poop-poop ! . . . Poop-poop ! . . . Poop-poop !

MOLE.   What's he saying ?

RAT.   I *think* he thinks he's the motor-car.

TOAD.   Poop-poop !

MOLE (*soothingly*).   It's all right, Mr. Toad.   It's all
right now.

RAT.   We'll make 'em sit up, Toad.   We'll have the
law of 'em.   We'll get you another little cart—we'll
make 'em pay for it.

ALFRED.   Another !   Oh, thank you, thank you,
not at all, don't mention it, only too delighted.

TOAD.   Poop-poop ! . . . (*Raptly he speaks*) Glorious,
stirring sight !   The poetry of motion !   The *real* way
to travel !   The *only* way to travel !   Here to-day—in
the middle of next week to-morrow !   Villages skipped,
towns and cities jumped—always somebody else's
horizon.   Oh bliss, oh rapture !   Oh poop-poop !

RAT.   Oh, stop being an ass, Toad !

TOAD (*dreamily*).   And to think that I never knew !
All those wasted years that lie behind me, I never knew,
never even dreamt.   But now that I know, now that I
fully realize—ah, now !   Oh what a flowery track lies
spread before me henceforth !   What savoury dust-
clouds shall spring up behind me as I speed on my
reckless way, what luscious and entrancing smells.
What carts I shall fling carelessly into the ditch in the
wake of my magnificent onset.   Horrid little carts—
common carts—canary-coloured carts !

RAT.   Now, look here, Toad, pull yourself together.
We'll go to the police-station, and see if they know
anything about that motor-car, and then we'll lodge a
complaint against the owners, and we'll go to a wheel-

wright's and have the cart fetched and mended and put to rights, and we'll——

TOAD. Police-station? Complaint! *Me* complain of that beautiful, that heavenly vision which has been vouchsafed me? *Mend* the *cart*? I've done with carts for ever. Horrid little carts, common carts, canary-coloured carts!

MOLE (*hopelessly*). What are we to do with him?

TOAD. Oh, Ratty! Oh, my good friend Mr. Mole! You can't think how obliged I am to you for coming with me on this glorious trip. I wouldn't have gone without you, and then I might never have seen that— that swan, that star, that thunderbolt. I might never have heard that entrancing sound, nor smelt that bewitching smell! I owe it all to you, my dear, my very dear friends.

RAT (*sadly*). I see what it is. I recognize the symptoms. He is in the grip of a new craze.

> [*Faintly the* FERRETS *and the* STOATS *and the* WEASELS *are heard singing :*

Down with Toad! Down with Toad!
Down with the popular, successful Toad!

TOAD (*raptly*). Poop-poop!

RAT (*to* MOLE). Well, come along. Let's get him home.

MOLE. Come on, Alfred.

ALFRED (*sadly*). One of the most distressing cases which has come under our notice. Very sad! Very sad!

TOAD. Poop-poop!

> [*They trudge off. As soon as they are gone, the Bank is alive again with the* WILD-WOODERS, *who burst into mocking laughter.*

ACT II

SCENE I

The Wild Wood

SCENE.—*The middle of the Wild Wood. It is an awesome place in the moonlight, with the snow thick upon the ground; cold, silent, threatening. Yet not altogether silent, that is the worst of it. You feel that there are hidden watchers behind the trees, waiting to jump out at you; you hear, or seem to hear, their stealthy movements. There is a sudden rustling . . . and then silence. A twig cracks. Somebody is breathing. . . .*

Now at last we can recognize somebody. It is TOAD, *in motoring gloves and goggles, coming anxiously through the trees, with many a sudden stop and furtive glance over his shoulder. We can hear, and he hears too, a murmur of unseen voices, which rises in a sort of chant until at last we can distinguish the words.*

CHORUS OF WILD-WOODERS:

    Toad! Toad! Down with Toad!
    Down with the popular, successful Toad!

TOAD (*alarmed*). W-what's that?
                [*Mocking laughter answers him.*
Pah!   [*Dead silence.*
I said ' Pah! ' (*Nervously*) A-and ' Bah! ' (*Loudly*)

25

Bah ! (*There is an echoing 'Bah'*.)   What's that ? (*Again the echo of the last word comes back to him, and he laughs, but a little uneasily*.)   Silly of me.   Just an echo.   Something to do with the acoustics.   I must tell Rat.   He'd be interested.

CHORUS (*softly*) :

Toad !   Toad !   Down with Toad !
Down with the gallant and courageous Toad !

TOAD (*sharply*).   Who said that ?
[*Mocking laughter answers him.*
I can see you.   [*Dead silence.*
Very funny, aren't you ?   I suppose you think I'm afraid ?   (*Loudly*) I said I suppose you think I'm *afraid* ?   (*There is an echoing 'afraid'*.)   There you are, it's nothing.   Just an echo.   Listen.   (*Hand to mouth*) Rat !   (*Dead silence*.)   Perhaps it doesn't work sometimes.   Something to do with the direction of the wind.   I'll try again.   (*Very loudly*) RAT !
A SOLEMN VOICE.   Mole !
[*And then a burst of laughter.*

CHORUS (*in quick, business-like time*) :

Toad !   Toad !   Down with Toad !
Down with the terrified and timorous Toad !

TOAD.   C-c-come and do it !   C-come and do it if you dare.   (*The mocking laughter again*.)   Yes, that's all you can do—laugh.   Any one can laugh.   Ha-ha-ha-ha-ha !   Very funny, isn't it ?
A VOICE.   Where are you going, Toad ?
TOAD.   Never you mind where I'm going.   I'm going to see Badger, that's where I'm going.   (*More*

confidently as he thinks of BADGER.)   My *friend*, Mr. Badger.   I'm calling on my old and valued boon-companion,
the fierce and terrible Badger !   [*Loud laughter.*

A LOW VOICE.   Where are you going to, my pretty
Toad ?

A HIGH VOICE.   Just a little way down the road.

A LOW VOICE.   Why are you wearing your bonnet
and shawl ?

A HIGH VOICE.   Because I am paying an evening
call.

A LOW VOICE.   Knock at the door, for here's the
house.

A HIGH VOICE.   Ah ! Good evening, Mr. Mouse !
                    [*There is another burst of laughter.*

A VOICE.   Badger doesn't live here, Toad !

TOAD (*desperately, greeting an imaginary friend*).
Yes, he does, there he is.   Ah, my dear Badger, how
are you ?   No, not at all.   Yes, delighted, quite so, no,
yes, not in the least.   Fancy !   Ha-ha !   Well, yes,
just a little walk through the wood.   Oh, do you think
so ?   And you're looking splendid yourself.   Never
saw you looking fiercer.   (*Loudly*) I said *fiercer* !   (*As
he goes off*) This way, my dear Badger !

A VOICE.   Good-bye, Toad !

A HIGH VOICE (*answering*).   Good-bye !

A VOICE.   Good-bye, Mouse.

A SQUEAKY VOICE (*answering*).   Good-bye !
        [*There is a last shout of laughter as* TOAD *dis-
            appears.*

CHORUS (*softly*) :

Toad !   Toad !   Down with Toad !
Chilblains and Mumps to the Miserable Toad !

Toad ! Toad ! Down with Toad !
Frostbite and Hiccups to the Miserable Toad !

[*The chant goes on, a murmur of unseen voices,
whose words we can no longer distinguish. In a
little while we can hear nothing, and yet it seems
that at any moment we shall hear something.
No wonder that* MOLE, *limping through the
trees, keeps looking over his shoulder.*

MOLE (*hopefully*). Ratty ! (*In sudden panic*) What's
that ? (*The movements stop.*) Pooh ! It's nothing !
I'm not frightened ! . . . I do wish Ratty were here.
He's so comforting, is Ratty. Or the brave Mr. Toad.
He'd frighten them all away. (*He seems to hear the
sound of mocking laughter.*) What's that ? (*He looks
round anxiously.*) Ratty always said, ' Don't go into
the Wild Wood.' That's what he always said. ' Not
by yourself,' he said. ' It isn't safe,' he said. ' We
never do,' he said. That's what Ratty said. But I
thought I knew better. There he was, dear old Rat,
dozing in front of the fire, and I thought if I just
slipped out, just to see what the Wild Wood was
like—— (*He breaks off suddenly and darts round,
fearing an attack from behind. There is nothing.*) I
should be safer up against a tree. Why didn't I think
of that before ? (*He settles himself at the foot of a tree.*)
Ratty would have thought of it, he's so wise. Oh,
Ratty, I wish you were here ! It's so much more
friendly with two !   [*His head droops on his chest.*

A VOICE (*from far off*). Moly ! Moly !
MOLE (*waking up suddenly*). What's that ?
A VOICE. Moly !
MOLE (*frightened*). Who is it ?

A Voice. Moly! Moly! Moly! Where are you?
It's me—it's old Rat!

[Rat *appears ; a lantern in his hand, a couple of*
pistols in his belt, and a cudgel over his shoulder.

Mole (*almost in tears*). Oh, Rat! Oh, Rat!

Rat (*patting him on the back*). There, there, there!

Mole. Oh, Ratty, I've been so frightened, you
can't think.

Rat. *I* know, *I* know. You shouldn't have gone
and done it, Mole. I did my best to keep you from it.
We River-Bankers hardly ever come, except in couples.

Mole. But *you've* come by *your*self. Ah, but then
that's because you're so brave.

Rat. It isn't just bravery, it's knowing. There
are a hundred things you have to know, which we understand about, and you don't as yet. I mean passwords
and signs, and sayings which have power and effect,
and plants you carry in your pocket, and verses you
repeat backwards, and dodges and tricks you practise ;
all simple enough if you know them, but if you don't,
you'll find yourself in trouble. Of course if you're
Badger, it's different.

Mole. Surely the brave Mr. Toad wouldn't mind
coming here by himself ?

Rat (*laughing*). Old Toad ? He wouldn't show his
face here alone, not for a whole hatful of guineas,
Toad wouldn't.

Mole. Oh, Rat! It is comforting to hear somebody laugh again.

Rat. Poor old Mole! What a rotten time you've
had. Never mind, we'll soon be home now. How
would a little mulled ale strike you—after you've got
into slippers, of course ? I made the fire up specially.

MOLE.   You think of everything, Ratty.

RAT.   Well, shall we start ?

MOLE.   Oh, Ratty.   I don't know how to tell you, and I'm afraid you'll never want me for a companion again, but I can't, I simply *can't* go all that way now.

RAT.   Tired ?

MOLE.   Aching all over.   Oh, Ratty, do forgive me. I feel as if I must just sit here for ever and ever and ever, and I'm not a bit frightened now you're with me—and—and I think I want to go to sleep.

RAT.   That's all right.   But we can't stop *here*. (*He looks round about him.*)   Suppose we go and dig in that mound there, and see if we can't make some sort of a shelter out of the snow and the wind, and have a good rest.   And then start for home a bit later on. How's that ?

MOLE (*meekly*).   Just as you like.

RAT.   Come on, then.

> [*He leads the way to the mound, and* MOLE, *following, trips up suddenly and falls over with a squeal.*

MOLE.   Oh, my leg !   Oh, my poor shin !   Oo !

RAT.   Poor old Mole, you don't seem to be having much luck to-day, do you ?   What is it ?   Hurt your shin ?   Let's have a look at it.

MOLE.   I must have tripped over a stump or something.   Oh my !   Oh my !

RAT.   It's a very clean cut.   That was never done by a stump.   Looks like the sharp edge of something metal.   Funny !

MOLE.   Well, never mind what done it.   It hurts just the same whatever done it.

RAT. Wait a moment.

> [*He begins scratching in the snow.*

MOLE. What is it ?

RAT. I thought so !

MOLE (*still nursing his leg*). What *is* it ?

RAT. Come and see.

MOLE (*hobbling up*). Hullo, a door-scraper ! How very careless of somebody !

RAT. But don't you see what it means ?

MOLE (*sitting down again and rubbing his shin*). Of course I see what it means. It means that some *very* forgetful person has left his door-scraper lying about in the middle of the Wild Wood just where it's sure to trip everybody up. Somebody ought to write to him about it.

RAT. Oh, Mole, how stupid you are. (*He begins scratching busily again.*) There ! What's that ?

MOLE (*examining it closely*). It looks like a door-mat.

RAT. It *is* a door-mat. And what does *that* tell you ?

MOLE. Nothing, Rat, nothing. Who ever heard of a door-mat telling any one anything ? They simply don't do it. They are not that sort at all. They— what have you found *now* ?

> [RAT, *still at it, has now disclosed a solid-looking little door, dark green, with a brass plate on it.*

RAT (*proudly*). There ! (*He fetches the lantern and holds it up to the plate.*) What do you read there ?

MOLE (*awestruck*). ' Mr. Badger. Seventh Wednesdays '. . . . Rat !

RAT (*proudly*). What do you think of *that* ?

MOLE. Rat, you're a wonder, that's what you are ! I see it all now. You argued it out step by step from the moment when I fell and cut my shin, and you looked

at the cut, and your majestic mind said to itself,
'Door-scraper'. Did it stop there? No. Your
powerful brain went on working. It said to itself——

RAT (*impatiently*). Yes, yes, well now let's——

MOLE (*going on sleepily and happily*). Your powerful
brain said to itself, 'Where there's a scraper, there must
be a mat.'

RAT. Quite so. And now——

MOLE :

> 'I have noticed before,' said the wise Mr. Rat,
> 'That where there's a scraper there must be
> a mat.'

And did you stop *there* ? No. Your intellect still
went on working. It said grandly to itself, 'Where
there's a door-mat there must be a door.'

RAT. Exactly. And now that we've found it——

MOLE :

> Said the wise Mr. Rat, ' I have noticed before,
> That where there's a door-mat there must be
> a door.'

You know, Rat, you're simply wasted here amongst
us fellows. If I only had your head——

RAT. But as you haven't, I suppose you are going
to sit on the snow and *talk* all night. Now wake up
a bit and hang on to this bell-pull, while I hammer.

MOLE (*sleepily*). Oh, all right !

> Said the wise Mr. Rat, ' I have often heard tell
> That where there's a bell-pull there *must* be
> a bell.'

> [*He hangs on to the bell-pull, while* RAT *hammers
> on the door with his cudgel. Down in* MR.
> BADGER'S *house a deep-toned bell responds.*

SCENE 2

Badger's House

SCENE.—BADGER'S *underground home. The room which we see is one of those delightful mixtures of hall, kitchen, drawing-room, dining-room, larder and pantry. In the middle of the room, says Mr. Kenneth Grahame, but we shall probably put it to one side, stands a long table of plain boards on trestles, with benches drawn up to it. There is a big open fireplace with high-backed settles on each side; an arm-chair in which the owner can read* The Times, *and is now so doing. The floor is brick; from the rafters hang hams, nets of onions and bundles of herbs. In short, a place where heroes can feast after victory, harvesters keep their Harvest Home with mirth and song, and two or three friends sit about as they please in comfort and content. There are three doors, labelled* FRONT DOOR, BACK DOOR, *and* STUDY. *At a knocking on the Back Door a convulsion passes over* The Times; *at a second knocking it stands on end; and at a third* MR. BADGER *comes out from behind the leading article. Grumbling to himself, for his after-supper nap has been disturbed, he goes to the door.*

BADGER (*opening the door*).   Well, well, well, what is it, what is it?

> [*A collection of* FIELD-MICE, *half a dozen of them in red mufflers, stand nervously shuffling at the entrance.*

D

FIRST FIELD-MOUSE (*huskily*). Oh, please, Mr. Badger, did you want any carols ?

BADGER. Any *what* ? Speak up !

FIRST FIELD-MOUSE (*swallowing*). Carols.

BADGER. Let's have a look at them.

SECOND FIELD-MOUSE (*striking up*). ' Good King Wenceslas looked out——'

BADGER. Oh, I thought you said carrots. Run along, all of you. Time you were in bed.

SECOND FIELD-MOUSE. ' Good King Wenceslas looked out——'

BADGER. And if you come round disturbing *me* again, *you'll* have to look out. Now then, off you go.

FIRST FIELD-MOUSE. Oh, please, Mr. Badger, we always used to sing carols to Mr. Mole, and he used to ask us in, and give us hot drinks, and supper too sometimes.

SECOND FIELD-MOUSE (*proudly*). We had steak-and-kidney pudding once.

FIRST FIELD-MOUSE. That's right, sir.

SECOND FIELD-MOUSE. Real steak - and - kidney pudding with kidney in it.

FIRST FIELD-MOUSE. That was Mr. Mole, sir. Down at Mole End. Always asked us in, Mr. Mole did.

BADGER. Ah ! Mole did, did he ? And Mole is a very sensible young animal. I have great hopes of Mole. Well, run away now, but come back in twenty minutes, when I'm not so busy, and perhaps I'll let you sing me the—what did you call it ?

FIELD-MICE (*eagerly*). Carol.

BADGER. Carol. I thought you said carrot. Well, then, you can sing me the one that Mr. Mole liked, and if I like it too, I won't say that perhaps there won't be a bit of hot something for one or two of you, the ones that don't snuffle, that is, and——

FIELD-MICE. Oh, thank you, Mr. Badger.

BADGER. Now then, run along, there's good children. (*They run along.*) So Mole likes carols, does he ? (*He goes back to his chair, and covers his face up again.*) Likes carols, does he ? (*He breathes heavily.*) Carols. . . . Thought he said carrots.

> [*He snores. . . . But he is not to sleep long. This time it is the front-door bell which rings ; again—and again. There is a hammering too, at the door. Very much annoyed,* BADGER *gets to his feet,*

BADGER. *All* right, *all* right, *all* right ! What is it, who is it ? (*He opens the front door.*) Speak up !

RAT. Hallo, Badger ! It's me, Rat, and my friend Mole, and we've lost our way in the snow, and Mole's that tired you never did.

BADGER. Well, well, well ! Rat and his friend Mole ! (*He brings them in.*) Come along in, both of you, at once. Why, you must be perished ! Well I never ! Lost in the snow ! And your friend that tired ! Well, well ! And in the Wild Wood at this time of night ! (*He pats their heads paternally.*) I'm afraid you've been up to some of your pranks again, Ratty. But come along in. There's a good fire here, and supper and everything.

MOLE (*as he sees the supper-table*). Oo, I say !

> [*He nudges the* RAT *in an anticipatory sort of way.*

BADGER. Now what will you do first ? Toast your toes a bit ? (*He removes* The Times.) I was just glancing at the paper.   Or supper now, and toast your toes afterwards ?   It's all ready.   I was expecting one or two friends might drop in.

MOLE (*shyly*).   I think I should like supper at once, please, Mr. Badger.

BADGER.   That's right, Mole.   Sensible animal.   And what about you, Rat ?

RAT (*who is standing with his back to the fire, as an old friend should*).   Just as you like.   Fine old place this, isn't it, Mole ?

MOLE (*already among the plates*).   Grand.

> [*He sits down to it.*   RAT *fetches himself a sand-wich and gets his back to the fire again.*   BADGER, *in an arm-chair, beams upon them kindly.*

BADGER (*to* RAT).   Won't your friend try some of those pickles ?

RAT.   Try a pickle, Mole.

MOLE (*his mouth full*).   Thanks.   [*He helps himself.*

BADGER (*solemnly, after a silence broken only by the noise of eating*).   I've been wanting to see you fellows, because I have heard very grave reports of our mutual friend, Toad.

RAT (*sadly*).   Oh, Toad !   [*He shakes his head.*

MOLE (*as sympathetically as he can with a mouth full of pickles*).   Tut-tut-tut.

BADGER.   Is his case as hopeless as one has heard ?

RAT.   Going from bad to worse—that's all you can say about him, isn't it, Mole ?

MOLE (*nodding busily*).   'M !   (*Swallowing hastily.*)   That's all.

RAT.   Another smash-up only last week, and a bad one.   You see, since he's got this motor craze, he will insist on driving himself, and he's hopelessly incapable.

If he'd only employ a decent, steady, well-trained animal, pay him good wages and leave everything to him, he'd get on all right. But no ; he's convinced he's the greatest driver ever, and nobody can teach him anything. And so it goes on.

MOLE. And so it goes on.

BADGER (*gloomily*). And so it goes on ! (*After a pause*) How many has he had ?

RAT. Cars or smashes ? Oh well, it's the same thing with Toad. The last was the seventh.

MOLE. He's been in hospital three times, and as for the fines he's had to pay——

RAT. Toad's rich, we all know, but he's not a millionaire. Killed or ruined, it will be one or the other with Toad.

BADGER. Alas, alas ! I knew his father, I knew his grandfather. Many's the time—— (*A sob chokes him.*) Alas, poor witless animal !

MOLE (*still busy*). You really ought to try a slice of this beef, Rat.

RAT. No, thanks, really.

MOLE. Don't know when I've tasted better.

RAT (*to* BADGER). Oughtn't we to *do* something ? We're his friends.

BADGER. Yes, you're right. The hour has come.

MOLE (*anxiously*). What hour ?

BADGER. Whose hour, you should say. Toad's hour. The hour of Toad.

RAT (*quietly*). Well done, Badger. I knew you'd feel that way too.

MOLE (*firmly*). *We'll* teach him to be a sensible Toad.

BADGER. At any moment another new and exceptionally powerful motor-car will arrive at Toad Hall for approval or return. We must be up and doing ere it is too late.

RAT. That's right, Badger. We'll rescue the poor unhappy animal! We'll convert him! He'll be the most converted Toad that ever was before we've finished with him.

BADGER. The first step is to get him here and reason with him. You know how it is. In the present weather, I don't go about much. Naturally.

RAT. Of course not.

MOLE. Of course not.

BADGER. But once Toad is here——

RAT. How to get him, that's the problem——

BADGER (*gravely*). Let us apply our minds to it.

[*They apply their minds. Absent-mindedly, while thinking,* MOLE *helps himself to beef. Suddenly the bell rings loudly.*

BADGER. Whoever's that?

[*He shuffles off to the door, and as he opens it,* TOAD *falls into his arms, panting with fear.*

RAT (*in surprise*). Why, it's Toad!

MOLE. Hallo, Toad, you ought to try some of this beef!

RAT. Why, what's the matter? (TOAD, *supported by* BADGER, *falls limply into a chair and sits there panting.*) Another accident? (TOAD *shakes his head.*) That's something.

TOAD (*still panting a little*). Ah, Ratty, my dear old Ratty, and my good friend Mole, how badly I seemed to need your help just now! What would I not have given to have had you by my side. As it was, I had to do the best I could without you.

Fortunately it was enough.   But as you see, it has exhausted me somewhat.

RAT.   What's happened ?   Wild-Wooders ?

TOAD (*warming to it*).   An unfortunate breakdown in my car—a loose nut, some trifling mishap—left me stranded at the edge of the wood, far from home.   I bethought me of my good friend Mr. Badger ; he would lend me a sleeping suit and put me up for the night.   As I came whistling through the wood, recking naught of danger, I was suddenly seized upon by a gang of rascally ferrets.   I set about them light-heartedly—at the most there were no more than a dozen of them—when suddenly, to my horror, they were reinforced by a posse of scoundrelly weasels. It was then, Ratty—and my dear friend Mole—that I wished I had your assistance.   Twelve of the rascals, yes (*he is now standing up, legs straddled, and enjoying himself immensely*), but twenty-four of them is a different matter.   If only you and Mole could have taken a couple of them off my hands, there might have been a different story to tell.   As it was, a rear-guard action was forced upon me.   Step by step—— (*He realizes a faint hostile something in the air, particularly from the direction of* BADGER.   *He goes on less confidently.*)   Step by step—— (*He looks from one to the other, hoping for a little encouragement, but the atmosphere is now really terrible ; nobody could tell even the simplest story in it.   He makes a last desperate effort.*)   Step by step——

BADGER (*solemnly*).   Won't you sit down again, Toad ?

TOAD (*meekly*).   Thank you.

RAT.   Would you care to be nearer the fire ?

TOAD (*faintly*).   No, thank you.

MOLE.   Let me put your gloves down for you.

TOAD.   It's all right, thank you.

BADGER (*to* RAT).   The moment has come, I think, don't you ?

RAT.   I think so.

BADGER (*to* MOLE).   You agree ?

MOLE.   Yes.   [*He sighs.*

TOAD (*uneasily*).   I say, you fellows, what's all this——

    [*He catches* BADGER'S *eye and is silent again.*

BADGER (*solemnly*).   Toad !   I knew your father, worthy animal that he was ; I knew your grandfather. It was also my privilege to be slightly acquainted with your uncle, the Archdeacon ; of that I shall speak further directly.   The question I wish to ask you now is this.   At the beginning of the breathless story of adventure to which we have just been listening, you mentioned (*he pauses dramatically*) a motor-car.   You implied further that this motor-car had suddenly lost its efficiency.   Am I right in supposing that just at this moment your narrative hovered for an instant on the confines of truth ?

TOAD (*sulkily*).   What do you mean ?

RAT.   Really, Toad, he couldn't have put it more plainly.

BADGER.   I asked you, Toad, if it is indeed a fact that your eighth motor-car is now in as fragmentary a condition as the previous seven ?

TOAD (*sulkily*).   I had a little accident.

BADGER.   Thank you.   (*To* RAT) Then I think that in that case we may begin the treatment ?

RAT.   Yes, I think so.

BADGER (*to* MOLE).   You agree ?

MOLE.   Yes.

TOAD.   I say, you fellows——

BADGER.   Toad ! (TOAD *looks at him.*)   Rise from your chair a moment. (TOAD *rises.*)   Rat, Mole, may I trouble you a moment ?   (*He indicates that he wants* TOAD'S *chair in a pos.tion where he can be harangued better.   They rise to move it.*)   Thank you. . . . There, I think. . . . Perhaps just a trifle more to the left. . . . Thank you.   Toad !

> [*He points to the chair and* TOAD *meekly creeps into it.*

RAT (*kindly*).   This is all for your good, Toady old man.

BADGER.   Now then, first of all take those ridiculous goggles off.

TOAD (*plucking up courage*).   Shan't !   What is the meaning of this gross outrage ?   I demand an instant explanation.

BADGER.   Take them off then, you two.

RAT (*as* TOAD *looks like showing fight*).   It's all for your own good, Toady old man.   We've been talking it over for hours.   Might as well take it quietly.

MOLE.   We don't like doing it, Toad, really we don't.   It's only because we are so fond of you.

> [*They remove the goggles.*

BADGER.   That is better.   It was thus that your father knew you.   It was thus that your grandfather, had he survived a year or two longer, would have known you.   Now then, Toad.   You've disregarded all the warnings we've given you, you've gone on squandering the money your father left you, and you're getting us animals a bad name in the district

by your furious driving and your smashes and your
rows with the police. We have decided, my friend
Ratty here and Mole and I, that it is time we saved
you from yourself. I am going to make one more
effort to bring you to reason. You will come with me
into my study, and there you will hear some facts
about yourself. I say the study, because on second
thoughts I have decided, for the sake of your revered
grandfather, to spare you the pain of a public reproof.
Come !

TOAD (*meekly*). Yes, Badger. Thank you, Badger.
[*They go out together.*

RAT. That's no good ! Talking to Toad will never
cure him. He'll *say* anything.

MOLE. Yes.   [*He sighs.*

RAT. We must *do* something.

MOLE. Yes.   [*He sighs again.*

RAT (*looking at him suddenly*). What's the matter,
old fellow ? You seem melancholy. Too much beef ?

MOLE (*bravely*). Oh, no, it isn't that. It was just
—no, never mind, I shall be all right directly.

[*He wipes away a tear.*

RAT. Why, whatever is it ?

MOLE. Nothing, Ratty, nothing. I was just ad-
miring Badger's great big house and comparing it
with my own little home, which—which I haven't
seen lately—just comparing it, you know, and thinking
about it—and thinking about it—and comparing it.
Not meaning to, you know. Just happening to—think
about it.

RAT (*remorsefully*). Oh, Mole !

MOLE (*in a sudden burst*). I know it's a shabby,
dingy little place ; not like your cosy quarters, or

Toad's beautiful Hall, or Badger's great house—but it was my own little home—and I was fond of it—and I went away and forgot all about it—and since we've been down here it's all been coming back to me—perhaps it's the pickles—*I* always had Military Pickles too—I shall be better soon—I don't know what you'll think of me.

RAT (*patting him on the back*). Poor old Mole ! Been rather an exciting day, hasn't it ? And then the same sort of pickles. Tell me about Mole End. We might go and pay it a visit to-morrow if you've nothing better to do.

MOLE. It wouldn't be fine enough for *you*. You're used to great big places and fine houses. I noticed directly we came in how you stood with your back to the fire so grandly and easily, just as if it were nothing to you.

RAT. Well, *you* tucked into the beef, old chap.

MOLE. Did I ?

RAT. Rather ! Made yourself quite at home. I said to myself at once, ' Mole is used to going out,' I said. ' Week-end parties at big country houses,' I said, ' that's nothing to Mole,' I said.

MOLE (*eagerly*). Did you really, Ratty ?

RAT. Oh, rather ! Spotted it at once.

MOLE. Of course there *were* features about Mole End which made it rather—rather——

RAT. Rather a feature ?

MOLE. Yes. The statuary. I'd picked up a bit of statuary here and there—you'd hardly think how it livened the place up. Garibaldi, the Infant Samuel, and Queen Victoria—dotted about in odd corners. It had a very pleasing effect, my friends used to tell me.

RAT (*heartily*). I should like to have seen that, Mole, I should indeed. That must have been very striking.

MOLE. It was just about now that they used to come carol-singing.

RAT. Garibaldi—and the others ?

MOLE. The field-mice.

RAT. Oh yes, of course.

MOLE. Quite an institution they were. They never passed me over—always came to Mole End last, and I gave them hot drinks, and supper sometimes, when I could afford it.

RAT. Yes, I remember now hearing about it, and what a fine place Mole End was.

MOLE (*wistfully*). Did you ? . . . It wasn't very big.

RAT. Between ourselves, I don't much care about these big places. Cosy and tasteful, that's what I always heard about Mole End.

MOLE (*squeezing* RAT's *paw*). You're a good friend, Ratty. I like being with *you*.

RAT. Good old Mole !

> [*They are happily silent together. Suddenly, faint and far-off and sweet, a carol can be heard . . . ' the carol that Mr. Mole liked '.*

MOLE. There they are !

> [*They listen raptly. When it is over they give a little sigh : for it is time now to get back to business. The door opens and* BADGER *comes in, leading by the paw a very dejected* TOAD.

BADGER (*kindly*). Sit down there, Toad. (TOAD *sits down.*) My friends, I am pleased to inform you that Toad has at last seen the error of his ways. He

is truly sorry for his misguided conduct in the past,
and he has undertaken to give up motor-cars entirely
and for ever in the future. I have his solemn promise
to that effect.

MOLE (*eagerly*). Oh, Toad, I *am* glad !

RAT (*doubtfully*). H'm !

BADGER. There is only one thing which remains
to be done. Toad, I want you solemnly to repeat
before your friends here what you fully admitted to
me in the study just now. First, you are sorry for
what you have done and see the folly of it all ?

[*There is an anxious silence.*

TOAD (*suddenly*). No ! I'm *not* sorry. And it
wasn't folly at all. It was simply glorious !

BADGER (*horrified*). What ?

MOLE. Toady !

RAT. I thought so.

BADGER. You back-sliding animal, didn't you tell
me just now in there——

TOAD. Oh yes, yes, in *there*. I'd have said anything in *there*. You're so eloquent, dear Badger, and
so moving, and so convincing, and put all your points
so frightfully well—you can do what you like with
me in *there*. But, thinking it over out *here*. I see that
I am not a bit sorry really, so it's no earthly good
saying I am ; now is it ?

BADGER. Then you don't promise never to touch
a motor-car again ?

TOAD. Of course I don't. On the contrary, I
faithfully promise that the very first motor-car I see
—Poop-poop, off I go in it !

RAT (*to* MOLE). I told you so.

BADGER. Very well then. Since you won't yield

to persuasion, we'll try what force can do. I feared
it would come to this all along. You'll stay with me,
Toad, until a cure has been effected. My friends, Rat
and Mole, will also stay with me and help me to look
after you. It's going to be a tedious business, but we
will see it out. (*He takes down a large key from the
wall, and picking up the lantern leads the way to the
guest-chamber.*) Bring him along.

[*They bring him along. The procession goes
slowly, and on* TOAD'S *part reluctantly, out.*

Scene 3

The same. Some weeks later

Scene.—*Badger's home on a spring morning some weeks later.* Mr. Badger *is in an arm-chair, with his feet on another, reading a newspaper, and paying no attention whatever to* Toad, *who is in the paroxysms of another attack.* Toad (*poor fellow*) *has arranged three chairs in a hopeful representation of a motor-car. He sits on the front one, grasping an imaginary wheel, changing imaginary gears, and making appropriate noises. A sudden (imaginary) block in the traffic pulls him up sharply, though his ' Hi, look ahead there ! ' averts an accident. He gets off and winds up his engine, then lifts the bonnet and peers in. In a little while he is off again ; but now a real accident upsets him. The chairs are strewn about and* Toad *lies panting in the wreckage.* Badger *lifts an eye, glances at him and goes on with his paper.* Mole *comes in. He looks at* Toad.

Mole. Tut-tut ! Again ?

Badger (*still reading his paper*). The third crash this morning. There seems to be a good deal of traffic on the road to-day.

Mole. Poor old Toad !

Badger. I always warned you, my dear Mole, that in these cases the poison takes a long time to work itself out of the system. But we're improving ; we're improving daily. Let me see. It's Rat's turn to be on guard this morning, isn't it ?

Mole. Yes. (*He helps* Toad *up.*) Lean on me,

old fellow. That's right. Lie down a bit. (*He assists him towards a camp-bed in the corner of the room.*) You'll be better directly. I dare say Rat will read to you, if you ask him.

TOAD (*weakly*).   Thank you, my dear friend, thank you.   Don't let me be a burden to you.

MOLE.   That's all right, Toady.   We'll soon get you well.

BADGER.   What do you say to a bit of a ramble along the hedgerows, Mole.   And there's a new burrow I want to show you.   I must say I like being out in this sort of weather.

MOLE (*eagerly*).   Just what I was going to suggest. I wish old Ratty could come too.   I suppose——

[*He looks across at* TOAD.

BADGER.   No, no, it wouldn't be safe. (*In a whisper*) Toad's quiet now, and when he is quiet, then he's at his artfullest.   I know him.

MOLE.   Yes, I suppose so.   But it's such an exciting sort of day.   Rat would love it so.

Enter RAT.

RAT.   Hallo, you fellows, not off yet ?

BADGER.   Just going. (*He gets up.*) Toad's quiet now.   But keep an eye on him.   I don't trust him.

RAT.   That's all right.

MOLE (*quietly to* RAT).   I believe he's worse than Badger thinks.   Look after him well, poor old Toad.

RAT.   That's all right.

BADGER (*at the door*).   Coming, Mole ?

MOLE.   Coming.   Poor old Ratty, it is a shame being kept in like this.   Still we all have our turns.

RAT.   Of course we do.   Good luck to you.

MOLE. Good-bye!

BADGER. Are you coming, Mole?

MOLE. Coming! Good-bye! Good-bye, Toad!

TOAD (*faintly*). Good-bye, dear old Mole.

MOLE (*ecstatically*). What a morning! I don't think I ever remember——

BADGER (*severely*). When I was young, we *always* had mornings like this.

> [*They go out.* RAT, *after getting into an easier coat turns his attention to* TOAD.

RAT. Well, how are you to-day, old chap?

TOAD (*faintly*). Thank you so much, dear Ratty. It is good of you to inquire. But first tell me how you are yourself?

RAT. Oh, *I'm* all right.

TOAD. I'm glad! I'm glad! And the excellent Mole?

RAT. Oh, *he's* all right.

TOAD. Splendid, splendid! And the venerable Badger? He, I trust, is in robust health also?

RAT. Rather! He and Mole have gone out for a ramble together. They won't be back till lunch.

TOAD. Ah! (*Very faintly*) Dear fellows all!

RAT. Now, old boy, we're going to have a jolly morning together, so jump up, and I'll do my best to amuse you.

TOAD. Dear, kind Rat, how little you realize my condition, and how very far I am from jumping up now—if ever. But do not trouble about me. I hate being a burden to my friends, and I do not expect to be one much longer.

RAT. Well, I hope not too. You've been a fine bother to us all *this* time, you have really, Toad.

E

Weeks and weeks ! And now, in weather like this, and the boating season just beginning ! It's too bad of you !

TOAD. I'm a nuisance to my friends, I know, I know.

RAT (*wistfully*). I was thinking about my river yesterday evening, and I—I wrote a little poem. (*Shyly*) Do you think you would like to hear it ?

TOAD. As you will, my dear Ratty. It may comfort my last hours.

RAT (*eagerly*). It's about the ducks. I used to have such fun with them. You know when they stand on their heads suddenly, well, then I dive down and tickle their necks, and they come up all spluttering and angry, and shaking their feathers at me—of course they aren't angry really, because it's all fun— and then I used to sit on the bank in the sun, and pretend I was coming in after 'em again, and—— (*He breaks off suddenly and announces*) ' Ducks' Ditty ' !

> All along the backwater,
>   Through the rushes tall,
> Ducks are a-dabbling,
>   Up tails all !
>
> Ducks' tails, drakes' tails,
>   Yellow feet aquiver,
> Yellow bills all out of sight
>   Busy in the river !
>
> Every one for what he likes !
>   We like to be
> Heads down, tails up,
>   Dabbling free !

High in the blue above
Swifts whirl and call—
We are down a-dabbling—
Up tails all !

[*He looks in front of him, seeing it all.*

TOAD (*with a deep sigh*). Thank you. I am glad to have heard it. . . . Ratty ?

RAT (*waking from his reverie*). Yes ?

TOAD. I wonder if I could bother you—but no, you have been too kind already.

RAT. Why, what is it ? You know we'd do anything for you, all of us.

TOAD. Then could I beg you, for the last time probably, to step round to the village as quickly as possible—even now it may be too late—and fetch the doctor ?

RAT (*surprised*). But——

TOAD. No, you're right. It's only a trouble, and perhaps we may as well let things take their course.

RAT. But what do you want a doctor for ?

TOAD. Surely you have noticed—— But no, why should you ? Noticing things is only a trouble. To-morrow, indeed, you may be saying to yourself, ' Oh, if only I had noticed sooner ! If only I had *done* something ! Too late, too late ! ' . . . Forget that I asked. Naturally you want to go on with your poetry. Have you ever done anything in the way of epitaphs ?

RAT (*alarmed*). Look here, old man, of course I'll fetch a doctor to you, if you really want one. But it hasn't come to that yet. You're imagining. Now let's talk about something more cheerful.

TOAD (*with an angelic expression*). I fear, dear
friend, that talk can do little in a case like this—or
doctors either, for that matter. Still, one must grasp
at the slightest straw. And by the way—while you
are in the village—I hate to bother you, but I fancy
that you pass the door—*would* you mind asking my
lawyer to step up? There are moments—perhaps I
should say there is *a* moment—when one must face
disagreeable tasks, at whatever cost to exhausted
nature. Thank you, my dear fellow, thank you.
You will not be forgotten.   [*He closes his eyes.*

RAT. A lawyer! He *must* be bad. (*Aloud*) All
right, Toad, I'll go.

    [*He makes his preparations to go out, glancing*
       from time to time at the unconscious TOAD *as*
       he does so. Then a brilliant idea occurs to him.

RAT (*loudly*). I'm going now, Toad.

TOAD (*faintly, his eyes closed*). Thank you, thank
you!

RAT. I'll bring the doctor and the lawyer, and
we'll be back as quickly as we can.

TOAD. You're a good fellow, Ratty.

RAT. Good-bye, old boy. Keep your spirits up.

TOAD. Good-bye!

    [*Humming a tune and making a good deal of*
      noise, RAT *goes out. Then very quietly he*
      steals back again and peers round the door.
      TOAD *is apparently still on the verge of dissolu-*
      tion. RAT *nods to himself in satisfaction*
      with his strategy; TOAD'S *illness is obviously*
      genuine We hear him as he starts through
      the Wild Wood, singing 'Ducks' Ditty' to
      himself. As the song dies in the distance,

> TOAD *opens an eye. Then the other eye. He raises his head and listens. He sits up in bed, still listening. Then with a laugh he jumps up and takes the floor.*

TOAD (*boastfully*). Ha, ha, ha! Smart piece of work that! (*He chatters to himself as he collects his coat, gloves, goggles, money, and other accessories of outdoor life.*) Brain against brute force—and brain came out on the top—as it's bound to do. Poor old Ratty! My! Won't he catch it when Badger gets back! A worthy fellow, Ratty, with many good qualities, but very little intelligence—and absolutely no education. I must take him in hand some day, and see if I can make something of him.

> [*He is ready now; as he goes to the door he begins to sing. Really a most conceited song:*

The world has held great heroes,
  As history-books have showed;
But never a name to go down to fame
  Compared with that of Toad!

> [*He is singing the last line as he opens the door. Then with a triumphant 'Poop-poop! Poop-poop!' he disappears.*

ACT III

SCENE I

The Court-House

SCENE.—*The Court-House. A bare, clean, white-washed room, furnished with a Bench, a Jury-Box, and a little extra space for the witnesses and spectators. It is crowded to-day, for the notorious* TOAD *is to be tried, and there is every prospect that he will be sentenced to a severe term of penal servitude. In one corner, sitting gloomily together, are* BADGER, RAT, *and* MOLE. BADGER *has his handkerchief out. On the Bench the* JUDGE, *an owl-like gentleman, is sitting, sipping a cup of tea. A figure, its head bowed in its hands, sits beside him. An* USHER, *tall and thin, wanders round the room with a list in his hand, ticking off those present. In the Jury-Box a* TURKEY, *a* DUCK, *four* SQUIRRELS, *five* RABBITS *and the* CHIEF WEASEL *are crowded together.*

USHER. One Judge. (*He looks at the Bench and marks off the* JUDGE *on his list.*) Twelve Jury. (*He counts them and marks them off.*) One policeman witness. (*To* POLICEMAN) That's you. Now, don't you go a-moving or you'll muddle me. One policeman, and one prisoner. (*He looks at the Dock.*) Hallo ! That's funny. Where is the prisoner ?

POLICEMAN (*staggered*). Well, I know I brought him in. (*Loudly*) Toad! Where are you?

TOAD (*looking up from the Bench, sadly*). Here I am.

USHER. What yer doing there? Come down out of it!

TOAD (*meekly*). I thought this was where the prisoners went.

> [*He glances at the* JUDGE, *and comes down with a smirk.*

EVERYBODY. Did you hear what he said. . . . . What was it? . . . Well, of all the cheek. . . . Just like Toad. . . . What was it? I didn't hear. . . .

> [*And now, all being present, the* USHER *walks up to the* JUDGE *and whispers in his ear. The* JUDGE *finishes his tea, and nods.*

USHER. Silence!

EVERYBODY (*to everybody else*). Silence! Silence! Silence! . . .

JUDGE (*annoyed*). Stop saying 'Silence!'

EVERYBODY (*to everybody else*). Stop saying 'Silence'.

JUDGE. It's worse than ever! (*To* USHER) Try them with 'Hush'.

USHER (*in a loud whisper*). Hush!

> *Everybody hushes.*

JUDGE. Please understand, once and for all, that unless I have complete hush, it will be impossible for the prisoner to be tried.

TOAD. I don't want to be tried.

JUDGE (*sternly*). Impossible for him to be tried, but not impossible for him to be severely sentenced.

BADGER (*in tears*). Alack! Alack! Oh, hapless Toad!

TOAD. Well, it was fun anyway.

JUDGE (*clearing his throat*). H'm ! Friends and fellow-citizens ! We see before us, cowering in the Dock, one of the most notorious and hardened male-factors of our time, the indigenous Toad.

TOAD. I'm not indigenous.

JUDGE (*grimly*). Well, if you're not, you very soon will be. We see before us, I say, this monster of iniquity, and it is our duty to try him fairly and without prejudice, and to sentence him to the very sharpest term of imprisonment that we can think of, so as to learn him not to do it again. We shall then adjourn for lunch. (*Cries of ' Hear, hear ! '*) It may be that after lunch we shall see things in a more rosy light, and be tempted to dilute justice with mercy, to the extent of remitting some thirty or forty years of the sentence. If so, we shall fight against the tempta-tion. If, on the other hand, we see things in a more sombre light, and realize suddenly that we have been too lenient with the cowering criminal before us, we shall not hesitate to remedy our error. (*Kindly*) Has the prisoner anything to say before we pass on ?

TOAD (*meekly*). No.

JUDGE. Very well. Then I proceed to the charge. The counts against the prisoner are as follows. (*To* USHER) By the way, is the Jury all present ? I particularly want the Jury to hear this. Just call 'em out and see.

USHER. Certainly, m'lord. . . . Mr. Turkey.

TURKEY. Here !

USHER. Mr. Duck.

DUCK. Here !

USHER. Four squirrels !

Squirrels.   Here !

Usher.   Six rabbits !

Rabbits.   Here ! [Rat *rises and holds up his hand*.

Rat (*firmly*).   I object.   [*Sensation*.

Judge (*putting on his glasses*).   What's the matter ?
Who is it ?   What did he—— Ah, Ratty, my little
friend, is it you ?   Delighted to see you.   If you will
just wait until I have got this ruffian off my hands,
we can have a little talk.   What about lunching with
me ?   (*To* Usher) Go on, please.

Usher.   Six rabbits !

Rabbits.   Here !

Rat.   I object, my lord.

Judge (*surprised*).   Object ?

Rat.   One of the rabbits is a weasel.

Chief Weasel (*indignantly*).   I'm not !   I'm a
rabbit.

Rat.   He's a weasel.

Judge.   Dear, dear !   A difference of opinion.   (*To*
Usher) What are we to do ?   What *does* one do ?

Usher.   He *says* he's a rabbit, my lord, and he
ought to know.

Judge (*to* Rat).   There's something in that.   You
can't make a mistake about a thing of that sort.

Rat (*doggedly*).   He's a weasel.

Chief Weasel.   I'm not !

Rat.   That proves it.   (*To* Weasel) Why should
you say you aren't, if you aren't ?

Judge.   But of course he says he aren't if he aren't.
I mean *if* he aren't, then he aren't, so naturally he
says he aren't.

                    [*He fans himself with his handkerchief*.

Rat.   But he wouldn't *say* he wasn't, if he wasn't.

The other rabbits didn't say they wasn't. Why didn't they say they wasn't ? Because they aren't.

JUDGE (*to* USHER). Just make a note that I shall want a glass of iced water if this goes on.

RAT (*eagerly*). Of course if you aren't, you don't say you aren't, but if you weren't, you would say you were.

JUDGE (*completely muddled*). But you wouldn't say you aren't, if you weren't, and on the other hand—— (*Despairingly*) I think we'd better begin this trial *all* over again.

USHER. Yes, my lord. Much the best way.

JUDGE (*to* RAT). You can tell me your objections afterwards, when we have this desperate ruffian safely lodged in a dungeon.

RAT. He's a weasel ! I know he's a weasel ! You can see he's a weasel ! It isn't fair !

JUDGE (*soothingly*). There, there, there ! We'll talk about it calmly at lunch. There's a nice saddle of mutton—and red-currant jelly.

MOLE (*boldly*). It's a shame, that's what it is, when everybody knows what the weasels *are*.

CHIEF WEASEL (*to the* RABBITS). I'm a rabbit, aren't I a rabbit ? (*Under his breath*) Say I am— quick !

RABBITS (*terrified*). Y-yes.

CHIEF WEASEL. There you are. Naturally there are lots of different kinds of rabbit, and I'm one of the different kinds.

RAT. No, you're not.

CHIEF WEASEL. Yes, I am.

JUDGE. Please, please ! For *my* sake. (*To* USHER) Now then, *all* over again.

USHER (*stolidly*). Mr. Turkey.

TURKEY. Here !

USHER. Mr. Duck.

DUCK. Here !

USHER. Four squirrels.

SQUIRRELS. Here !

USHER. Five ordinary rabbits.

RABBITS. Here !

USHER. One different kind of rabbit.

CHIEF WEASEL. Here !

USHER. That's the lot, my lord.

ALFRED (*suddenly appearing*). What about me ?

JUDGE (*putting on his glasses*). What *is* this ?

ALFRED (*in the* USHER'S *voice*). Alfred ! (*Squeakily*) Here !

JUDGE (*to the* POLICEMAN). Lead it out.

ALFRED (*as he is led out*). All right, all right. I only just looked in. No *esprit de corps*. That's what's the matter with them all. No *esprit de corps*.

JUDGE. Now then. (*Looking at his watch*) We haven't too much time. The counts against the prisoner are as follows : First, that he did maliciously steal a valuable motor-car without so much as a ' with your leave ' or a ' by your leave '. Second, that being in the said motor-car, he did drive recklessly and to the common danger. Third, that on being apprehended he was guilty of gross impertinence to the rural police. (*Cheerfully*) Now then, Toad, what have you got to say about all that ?

TOAD. I wasn't driving recklessly. I was just going along quietly at about seventy miles an hour, when I saw a policeman in front of me. Naturally I quickened up to see if he wanted anything. Same as any one else would have done who's fond of police-men.

POLICEMAN.   Recklessly *and* to the common danger.

TOAD.   Rubbish !

POLICEMAN.   And what did you call me, eh ?

TOAD.   How can I remember ?   Officer, constable, sergeant——

POLICEMAN.   No, you didn't.

JUDGE.   Now we're getting at it.   What did he call you ?

POLICEMAN (*annoyed*).   He called me fat-face.

[*Sensation.*

JUDGE (*aghast*).   Fat-face !

EVERYBODY (*to everybody else*).   He called him fat-face !

JUDGE.   This is terrible.   This adds years to my life.   (*To* POLICEMAN) You mean to tell me that this ruffian, this incorrigible rogue whom I am about to sentence to a severe term of penal servitude, had the audacity to call a representative of the Law ' fat-face ' ?

RAT.   Oh, Toady !

BADGER.   Alack ! Alack ! Oh, hapless animal !

JUDGE.   Fat-face ! Did I hear it aright ?   Fat-face ?

POLICEMAN (*sulkily*).   We don't want to make a song about it.   I told you what he called me, and that's what he called me.

USHER (*stolidly*).   Fat-face.

TOAD.   I didn't mean *him* any more than any one else.   I just murmured the expression to myself. It's a way I have.   I'm that sort of person.   I murmur things to myself.   It's the result of a highly-strung temperament and an artistic nature.

USHER. He admits that he passed the expression
' fat-face ', my lord, and that's good enough for any
ordinary jury.

CHIEF WEASEL. Speaking as a special kind of
rabbit, I say that it's good enough for *me*.

MOLE. Weasel !

CHIEF WEASEL. Shut up !

JUDGE. Very well. We have the prisoner con-
demned out of his own mouth of using most frightful
cheek to a member of the rural police. We shall now
sentence him severely.

USHER. Wait a bit, my lord. There's the little
matter of stealing a valuable motor-car without so
much as a ' with your leave ' or a ' by your leave '.

JUDGE. Does it matter ? I mean compared with
this unspeakable impertinence to which the prisoner
has already confessed ?

USHER. Well, it adds more to the sentence, like.

JUDGE. Ah, well, in that case we must certainly go
into the matter. Well, Toad, what have you got to
say about *that* ?

TOAD. I didn't mean to steal it. It was this way.
I was just having a bit of lunch at an inn. I had been
very ill—hadn't I, Ratty ?—and my dear friends Mr.
Rat and Mr. Mole and Mr. Badger had been looking
after me. It was the first time I'd been up and out,
and I was having my bit of lunch—just a round of
beef and a few pickled walnuts and a couple of helpings
of treacle pudding—when I heard outside ' Poop-
poop, poop-poop ! '

JUDGE. You heard *what* ?

TOAD (*raptly*). Poop-poop, poop-poop !

USHER (*stolidly*). Imitation of motor-car.

JUDGE. Oh! (*To himself*) Poop-poop! Poop-poop! (*Shaking his head*) No, I don't seem to get it.

TOAD. Well, then two gentlemen came in to lunch, and as soon as I'd finished mine I went out to look at their car. I thought there couldn't be any harm in my only just *looking* at it. So I looked at it. And then naturally I began to say to myself, ' I wonder if this car *starts* easily.' So I wound it up just to see. And then naturally I stepped into the driver's seat, just as I always do, and—and then I saw a policeman with a very fat fa—with a very nice expression, a very *handsome* policeman, and he said, ' You're going a hundred and seventy miles an hour ', and I said, ' Of course if you say so, dear Mr. Policeman ', and then——

JUDGE (*to* USHER). All this makes it worse, doesn't it ?

USHER. Much worse.

JUDGE (*relieved*). I thought so. It means we can give him a stiffer sentence ?

USHER. A much stiffer one.

JUDGE. Good. You were saying, Toad ?

BADGER (*rising weightily*). May *I* say a few words now, my lord ?

JUDGE. Who is this ?

USHER. Mr. Badger, a well-known and highly respected member of the community.

JUDGE. So it is, so it is, Well, Mr. Badger ?

BADGER. Alack ! Alack ! O hapless Toad ! O ill-fated animal.

JUDGE (*to* USHER). Is it a recitation ?

BADGER. I knew his father, I knew his grandfather, I knew his uncle, the Archdeacon.

JUDGE. This makes it very serious indeed.

BADGER. Many an afternoon have I spent in communion with his father at Toad Hall—one of the most attractive river-side residences with carriage-sweep.

JUDGE. Dear, dear! *With* carriage-sweep, you say?

BADGER. Unhappy day! O feckless Toad! O rash and ill-advised animal! [*He sits down again.*

JUDGE. Most interesting. We are all indebted to Mr. Badger for his profound and helpful observations. Now, I think, we can proceed to business.

CHIEF WEASEL. Guilty!

JUDGE. Of course he's guilty. That isn't the point. The only difficulty which presents itself in this otherwise very clear case is, how can we possibly make it sufficiently hot for the incorrigible rogue and hardened ruffian whom we see cowering in the Dock before us? Mr. Usher, will you please tell us what is the very stiffest penalty we can impose for each of the three offences for which the prisoner stands convicted? Without, of course, giving him the benefit of the doubt, because there isn't any.

USHER. Well, my lord, some people would consider that stealing a valuable motor-car was the worst offence, and so it is. But cheeking the police carries the severest penalty, and so it ought. Suppose you were to say a year for the theft, which is mild, and three years for the furious driving, which is lenient, and fifteen years for the cheek, which is purely nominal; those figures, if added together correctly, tot up to nineteen years——

JUDGE. First-rate!

USHER. So you'd better make it a round twenty and be on the safe side.

TOAD (*meekly*).   I don't mind if it isn't quite round.

JUDGE.   Silence !   An   excellent   suggestion,   Mr. Usher.   Now, prisoner, pull yourself together and try and stand up straight.   It's going to be twenty years for you this time.   And mind, if you appear before us again, on any charge whatever, we shall have to deal with you very seriously.

CHIEF WEASEL.   Hear, hear !

MOLE.   Shut up !

JUDGE.   Twenty years.   Don't forget.   Now then, prisoner, before the rest of us adjourn for lunch, is there anything you would like to say in the nature of a farewell speech ?   Any last words or valedictory utterances ?

TOAD (*boldly*).   Yes.

JUDGE (*kindly*).   Well, well, what is it ?

TOAD.   Fat-face !

JUDGE (*aghast*).   Fat-face ?   ME ?

TOAD (*wildly*).   All of you !   All the whole lot of you !   All fat-faces !   I am Toad, the Terror of the Highway ; Toad, the Traffic-queller, the Lord of the Lone Trail, before whom all must give way or be smitten into nothingness and everlasting night.   I am the Toad, the handsome, the popular, the successful Toad. And what are you ?   Just fat-faces.

JUDGE.   Well, of all the ungrateful things to say !

TOAD.   I am the great, the magnificent, the incomprehensible Toad !

RAT (*sadly*).   Oh, Toady, boasting again !

JUDGE.   To call *me*, after all I've done for him, fat-face !

TOAD.   The great Toad !

[*He breaks into his chant :*

F

> The world has held great heroes,
>   As history-books have showed ;
> But never a name to go down to fame
>   Compared with that of Toad !

JUDGE.   Silence !

TOAD :

> The clever men at Oxford
>   Know all there is to be knowed,
> But they none of them know one
>   half as much
>   As intelligent Mr. Toad !

JUDGE.   Stop him, somebody !   Stop him !

TOAD :

> The Army all saluted,
>   As they marched along the road ;
> Was it the King ? or Fat-face ?
>   No. It was Mr. Toad !

JUDGE.   Take him away !   Cast him into the dungeon !   Load him with chains !   Gag him !

EVERYBODY.   Now then !   Now then !   Better come quietly !

TOAD (*as he is hustled away*) :

> The Queen and her ladies-in-waiting
>   Sat in the window and sewed :
> She cried ' Look ! who's that *handsome*
>   man ?'
>   They answered, ' Mr. Toad.'

[*His voice is heard more and more faintly in the distance, as he is led to the dungeons :*
Mr. Toad !   Mr. Toad !   Mr. Toad !

Scene 2

The Dungeon

Scene.—*A Dungeon. On a heap of straw in the corner,* Toad *sleeps uneasily. The door is unlocked, and* Phoebe, *the jailer's daughter, comes in, with breakfast on a tray.* Toad *sits up and takes the straw from his hair.*

Phoebe. Good morning, Toad.

Toad (*gloomily*). Good morning, woman.

Phoebe. Slept well ?

Toad. Slept well ? How could I sleep well, immured in a dark and noisome dungeon like this ?

Phoebe. Well, some do. . . . See, I've brought your breakfast.

Toad. Then you will oblige me by taking it away again.

Phoebe. What—aren't you ever going to eat any more ?

Toad. You don't understand. This is the end.

Phoebe. You've said that every day for a month past. The end of what ?

Toad. The end of everything. At least it is the end of the career of Toad, which is the same thing. (*He paces up and down.*) The popular and handsome Toad, the rich and hospitable Toad, the Toad so free and careless and debonair !

Phoebe. Cheer up, there's always hope.

Toad. Hope ? How can I hope ever to be set at large again who have been imprisoned so justly for stealing so handsome a motor-car in such an audacious manner, and for such lurid and imaginative cheek bestowed upon such a fat, red-faced policeman ?

PHOEBE.   Well, there *is* that, of course.

TOAD.   Stupid animal that I was, now I must languish in this dungeon till people who were proud to say they knew me have forgotten the very name of Toad.

PHOEBE.   There's no need to languish *all* the time.

TOAD (*with sobs*).   Oh, wise old Badger ! (*To* PHOEBE) A friend of mine. . . . Oh, clever, intelligent Rat and sensible Mole !—two other friends.   What sound judgments, what a knowledge of men and matters you possess !   Oh, unhappy and forsaken Toad !

PHOEBE (*arranging the breakfast*).   Nice hot buttered toast and tea.

TOAD.   Oh, despairing and—— Did you say *hot* buttered ?

PHOEBE.   Made it myself, I did.   Father said, ' Here's the key of Number 87,' he said, ' and you can take him his breakfast.   He's the most notoriousest dangerous animal in the country,' said Father, ' and how we shall keep him under lock and key goodness only knows——'

TOAD (*brightening*).   Did he say that ?

PHOEBE.   His very words.   ' The most notoriousest dangerous *and* reckless animal within the four walls of this here castle.   And you can take him a couple of old crusts for his breakfast,' said Father, ' because I must starve and break his indomitable spirit,' said Father ; ' otherwise he'll get the better of me.'

TOAD (*making a great effort to be modest*).   Well, of course, one has one's reputation.

PHOEBE. So I said, ' Yes, Father,' and as soon as his back was turned I said to myself, ' What a shame ! ' and I made this nice buttered toast.

TOAD (*his mouth full of it*). Believe me, girl, I am not ungrateful. You must pay me a visit at Toad Hall one of these days. Drop in to tea one afternoon.

PHOEBE. Is that where you live ?

TOAD (*nodding*). Finest house in these parts for miles around.

PHOEBE. Tell me about it.

TOAD (*proudly*). Toad Hall is an eligible, self-contained gentleman's residence, very unique ; dating in part from the fourteenth century, but replete with every modern convenience. Up-to-date sanitation. Five minutes from church, post-office and golf-links. Approached by long carriage-sweep.

PHOEBE. Fancy ! And do your friends Mr. Badger and Mr. Rat and Mr. Mole live there with you ?

TOAD (*laughing heartily*). Oh, my dear child ! Badger ! Rat ! Mole ! Excellent fellows all, but hardly—how shall I put it ?—hardly (*with a wave of the paw*), well, hardly. They come to pay me a visit now and then, naturally ; always glad to see them ; but— well, quite frankly, they wouldn't be comfortable at a big house like Toad Hall, not to live. One has to be born to it. Badger lives in a rambling barn of a place near by ; Rat has a little river-side villa ; and Mole— well, really, I don't know where Mole does live. He's staying with Badger, I fancy, at present. Dear old Badger !

PHOEBE. You're feeling better, aren't you ?

TOAD. The artistic temperament. We have our ups and downs.   [*He returns to his breakfast.*

PHOEBE (*looking at him thoughtfully*). Now I wonder.

TOAD (*casually*). Any prisoners ever been known to escape from this castle of yours?

PHOEBE. Never.

TOAD (*a little dashed*). Oh! . . . Well, I must see what I can do. I must give my mind to it one day. Excellent buttered toast this.

PHOEBE. *I've* been giving my mind to it lately.

TOAD. That's the only way to make really good toast.

PHOEBE. I didn't mean to that. I meant to escaping. I think I see a way in which you might do it.

TOAD (*dropping his toast in his excitement*). You're going to help me?

PHOEBE. Yes. I like you, Toad, and I've felt sorry for you, and for your friends, who want to see you again so badly. And I think it's a shame the way you've been treated.

TOAD. They were afraid of me, that's what it was.
[*He puffs out his cheeks.*

PHOEBE. Now listen. I have an aunt who is a washerwoman.

TOAD (*kindly*). There, there! Never mind. Think no more about it. I have several aunts who *ought* to be washerwomen.

PHOEBE. Do be quiet a minute, Toad. You talk too much, that's your chief fault. Now my aunt does the washing for all the prisoners in the castle. Naturally we keep anything of that sort in the family. She brings the washing back Friday morning—that's to-day. Now you're very rich—at least you're always telling me so—and for a few pounds I think I could persuade her to lend you her dress and bonnet and so on, and you could escape as the castle washerwoman. You're very much alike in some ways—particularly about the figure.

TOAD (*indignantly*). We're *not*. I have a very elegant figure—for what I am.

PHOEBE. So has my aunt—for what *she* is. But have it your own way, you horrid proud ungrateful animal, when I'm trying to help you!

TOAD (*quickly*). Yes, yes, that's all right, thank you very much indeed. But I was only thinking—— You surely wouldn't have Mr. Toad, of Toad Hall, going about the country disguised as a washerwoman?

PHOEBE. All right, then you can stop here as a Toad. I suppose you want to go off in a coach and four?

TOAD. No, no! Please! You are a good, kind, clever girl, and I am indeed a proud and stupid Toad. Introduce me to your worthy aunt, if you will be so kind. It would be a privilege to meet her.

PHOEBE. That's better. (*As she goes out*) With a little trouble you'd make quite a nice Toad.

TOAD (*as the door closes*). Chit!

[*He bursts happily into his song again, as he arranges a little collection of money—notes, gold, and silver—on the table, in such a way that it looks like an accident rather than a bribe. PHOEBE returns with her AUNT, who appears to be dressed in a blanket. She has a bundle of clothes under her arm.*

PHOEBE. This is Mr. Toad. My aunt.

AUNT. Good morning.

TOAD (*in his society manner*). Good morning, dear

lady. Charming weather we are having, are we not?
Pray sit down. Your niece tells me that you—er—
attend to the—er—that is, you have under your charge
the habiliments, the more mutable habiliments of the
inhabitants of the castle. A delightful profession,
I am sure.

AUNT (*stolidly*, *to* PHOEBE). Is this the one?

PHOEBE. Yes.

AUNT (*to* TOAD). I wash.

TOAD. Quite so, quite so.

PHOEBE. I told you the idea, Aunt, didn't I?

AUNT (*eyeing the money*). Some of it.

> [*There is an awkward silence.* PHOEBE *catches*
> TOAD'S *eye and indicates the money.*

TOAD. Quite so. (*He clears his throat loudly.*) I
was wondering—naturally I shouldn't want to carry
all my money about with me—indeed, in the costume
suggested (*he indicates the bundle of clothes*)—I won-
dered if you would oblige me so far—purely as a favour
to *me*——

AUNT. Is that the money?

TOAD (*indicating the money on the table*). Just a
little—er—I haven't counted it——

AUNT. I have.

TOAD. Oh! . . . Well?

AUNT. Here you are.

> [*She hands over her bundle—cotton print gown,
> apron, shawl, and rusty black bonnet.*

TOAD (*seizing the bundle*). My dear lady, I am
eternally your debtor. Should you ever find yourself
in the neighbourhood of Toad Hall, a visit, whether
professional or social—— (*He holds up the dress.*) Er,
how do I——.

PHOEBE (*much amused*). I'll help you.

AUNT. You told him the condition?

TOAD. Condition?

PHOEBE. My aunt thinks she ought to be gagged and bound, so as to look as if she had been overcome. You'd like it, too. You wanted to leave the prison in style.

TOAD (*beamingly*). An excellent idea! So much more in keeping with my character.

AUNT. I brought a bit of rope along, in case like.

TOAD. Splendid!

AUNT (*enjoying it*). Got a nankerchief?

TOAD (*producing one*). Yes.

AUNT. Then you gags me first. (*In a hoarse whisper*) Help! Help! Help! Help! Help!

TOAD (*carried away by the realism of this*). Silence, woman, else I gag thee!

AUNT (*undeterred*). Help! Help! Help!

TOAD (*advancing with gag*). Thou hast brought it on thyself.   [*He gags her.*

AUNT (*pulling down gag*). A little tighter, I think. . . . Help! Help! Help!

TOAD (*pulling it tighter*). A murrain on thy cackling tongue! There! (*To* PHOEBE) Now then, lend a hand with this rope.

PHOEBE. How brave you are!   [*She lends a hand.*

TOAD (*regarding the* AUNT *with pride*). A neat bit of work that. Now then, how do I get into this?
                            [*He holds up the dress.*

PHOEBE. Silly, not like that. Here, give it to me. . . . Now then. (*She helps* TOAD *in, and does him up.*) Apron. . . . Shawl. . . . Now the bonnet.

There ! Well, upon my word, you're the very living image of her !

> [*The* Aunt *makes frantic indications of a desire to speak.*

Toad.   What's the matter with her ?

Phoebe.   She wants to say something, I think.

> [*She takes off the gag.*

Aunt (*with conviction*).   Too ugly.

Phoebe.   Who is ?

Aunt.   He is.

Toad.   My good woman——

Aunt.   Much too ugly.   Never do at all.

Toad (*amazed*).   Really——

Aunt.   Not a bit like me.   Not good-looking enough.

Toad.   Here, give me the gag !

Aunt.   Not *nearly* good-looking enough.   Not——

> [*But she is gagged again.*

Phoebe.   Now then, Toad, we must hurry.   I'll take you to the end of the corridor, and then you go straight down the stairs—you can't mistake the way—and if any of the jailers stop you and chaff you a bit —because she's very popular, Aunt is——

Toad (*coldly*).   I shouldn't have thought it.

Phoebe.   Then you must give them a bit of chaff back, but respectable, of course, being a widow woman with a character to lose.   Now good-bye and good luck.

Toad (*nervously*).   Good-bye, good-bye.   If you're ever in the neighbourhood of Toad Hall——

Phoebe.   Which I shan't be.   Now, come on, there's a good Toad.   You can thank me when you've escaped.   Now, don't forget—you're a washerwoman.

> [*She leads the way out.*

TOAD. Yes, yes, we must be off. (*Nervously*) I wish I knew a little more what washerwomen talked about. (*In a falsetto voice, as he goes*) I remember once when I was ironing a shirt-front——

SCENE 3

The Canal Bank

SCENE.—*Early morning. A quiet spot by the canal bank. The tow-path cuts along by the edge of a wood, in which, just here, is a little clearing. At the entrance, half in, half out of a big hollow tree, lies a heap of old clothing ; discarded, it would seem, by some washerwoman. . . . It moves. Evidently there is a washerwoman inside it. A voice comes from the interior. No, it is our friend* TOAD.

TOAD (*sleepily*). I'll wear the light brown suit, and tell the car to be round at eleven o'clock. . . . No, leave the blinds down.   [*He sleeps again.*
        [*Two baby rabbits come by with their* MAMA, *on their way to school.*
    FIRST BABY RABBIT (*Harold to the family*). What's 'at ?   [*He gazes at* TOAD.
    MAMA RABBIT. Now, now, come along, Harold, you'll be late for school.
    SECOND BABY RABBIT (*Lucy*). What's Harold doing ?
    HAROLD (*rooted to the hollow tree*). What is it ?
    MAMA RABBIT. Never mind now. Just some poor old washerwoman taking a rest. Come along, there's a good boy.
    HAROLD. May I play with it ?
    MAMA RABBIT. After school, perhaps.
    LUCY (*primly*). I like school. (*With an insufferable air of knowledge*) Twice two are four, twice three are six——

HAROLD. May I play with it now?

MAMA RABBIT. Not now, dear.

LUCY. What's Harold saying?

HAROLD. Do washerwomans know tables?

MAMA RABBIT. I expect they do.

LUCY (*proudly*). I know my twice times. Twice two are four, twice three are six——

HAROLD. What are washerwomans for?

MAMA RABBIT. Now, now, come along. (*She takes his hand.*) Now, Lucy. (*She takes* LUCY'S *hand.*) Now let's all run and see how quickly we can go.

> [*They scamper off.*

HAROLD (*as they go*). Why do washerwomans——

> [*But we hear no more.*

TOAD (*half waking again*). And tell Cook I'll have three eggs this morning, and be sure to give them each four minutes. . . . (*He moves and wriggles, and then slowly sits up.*) There, she's pulled the blinds up, and I told her—— Hallo! (*He looks round him in amazement.*) Wherever—— (*He stands up, looks at his clothes, looks round him again, and draws a deep breath of happiness.*) Aha! (*He chuckles.*) Toad again! Escaped from prison! Eluded his captors! Evaded his pursuers! The subtle and resourceful Toad!

> [*He sits down in the sun, and idly removes a few dead leaves from his person.*

> [*A* FOX *comes by, stops, and looks him up and down in a sarcastic sort of way.*

FOX. Hallo, washerwoman! Half a pair of socks and a pillow-case short this week. Mind it doesn't occur again. [*He goes off sniggering.*

TOAD. Silly joke! Where's the humour of it?

(*He stands up and spreads himself.*)   If he had known !
If he had only known who it was !   Not a common
washerwoman, but the great, the good, the entirely
glorious Toad !   (*He walks round and round in a circle,
chanting his song*) :

> The world has held great heroes,
>   As history-books have showed ;
> But never a name to go down to fame
>   Compared with that of Toad.

> The animals sat in the Ark and cried,
>   Their tears in torrents flowed ;
> Who was it said, ' There's land ahead ' ?
>   Encouraging Mr. Toad !

> The Queen and her ladies-in-waiting
>   Sat in the window and sewed ;
> She cried, ' Look, who's that *handsome*
>   man ? '
>   They answered, ' Mr. Toad.'

(*In an ecstasy*) Oh, how clever I am !   How clever, how
very clever—— (*He breaks off suddenly, as voices are
heard crying, ' Toad ! Toad ! There he is ! This
way ! '*)   Oh, misery !   Oh, despair !

> [*Terrified, he rushes into the hollow tree, and
>   burrows under the leaves.*

> [*The* JUDGE, *the* POLICEMAN, *the* USHER, *and
>   the* JAILER *come in.*

POLICEMAN.   This way, your lordship.   I heard him
singing.   All about himself.   Just about here it
sounded like.   [*He begins to look round.*

JUDGE. Not that revolting song he sang when I had the pleasure of sentencing him to twenty years in a dungeon?

POLICEMAN. That's the song, your lordship. Only he had a new verse to it. Three verses he sang altogether.

JUDGE. As conceited as the old ones?

POLICEMAN. Worse.

JUDGE. Dear, dear. (*To* USHER) What's the penalty for singing conceited songs about yourself? Can I give him another five years?

POLICEMAN. We've got to catch him first.

USHER. Two years a verse is the usual.

JUDGE. Good! Then that's six years. And say ten for having had the ingratitude to escape from a perfectly clean—(*to* JAILER) ventilated, you said?

JAILER. Well-ventilated.

JUDGE. Well-ventilated prison. That's another sixteen years. Excellent!

POLICEMAN. We've got to catch him first. But he's about here somewhere, that I do say.

JAILER. Just look in that hollow tree.

JUDGE. He wouldn't be there, would he? Such a silly place to hide in.

POLICEMAN. Well, you never know. (*He goes to it.* TOAD, *quaking in his fear, displaces the leaves.*) There's *something* there.

JUDGE. Something undoubtedly.

[*They all gather round.*

USHER. A bird of some sort, most like.

TOAD (*brilliantly*). Chirp! Chirp! Chirp!

POLICEMAN. Yes, you're right. Only a bird.

JUDGE. Only a bird. What a pity.

USHER. I knew it was only a bird. We're wasting time here.

JUDGE. True. Lead on, policeman.

POLICEMAN. Well, he's not far off. This way.

[*They all go off.*

[*The leaves move again, and then* TOAD'S *head peeps cautiously out.*

TOAD (*panting with fear*). Oh my! What an ass I am! What a conceited and heedless ass! Swaggering again! Shouting and singing songs again! Sitting about and gassing again! Oh my! (*He stands up and looks round cautiously. Then explores the clearing. The pursuit has died away.*) Ah! That was good! Just a little resource, a little cleverness! 'Only a bird.' Ha, ha, ha! That will amuse the dear old Badger. I can hear his hearty laugh. 'We're wasting time here.' How the dear fellow, Mole, will enjoy that! 'I knew it was only a bird.' The good Rat will chuckle when I tell him.

[*He is standing with his back to the tow-path. A horse, dragging a tow-rope, comes along the path, stops, and puts his head ingratiatingly over* TOAD'S *shoulder.* TOAD'S *jaw drops. His knees tremble.*

TOAD (*terrified*). All right! I'll come quietly. (*He looks nervously round, sees the horse, and gives a sob of relief.*) You quite startled me! I thought it was—— I said I'd come quietly, just to put him off his guard. That was all. Just to—— Hallo! (*He sees the rope.*) A barge! Aha! I will hail the owner and pitch him a yarn, and he will give me a lift by a route which is not troubled by fat policemen. Perhaps (*he heaves a sigh*) I may even get some breakfast!

[*The horse has stopped and is cropping the grass.
Evidently he is meant to stop here, for a com-
fortable-looking barge-woman comes in, carrying
a bag of corn.*

BARGE-WOMAN.   A nice morning, ma'am.

TOAD.   The same to you, ma'am.

BARGE-WOMAN (*holding up bag*).   Give the horse a
bit of breakfast.

TOAD (*with meaning*).   The horse ?

BARGE-WOMAN.   Had mine.

[*She ties the bag on to the horse's head.*

TOAD.   And a good hearty breakfast I'm sure it
was, ma'am.

BARGE-WOMAN.   Well, I won't deny I like my
vittals.

TOAD.   You're right, ma'am, you're right.   (*Casually*)
And finished it all up, I dare say—fried ham and eggs
and—all of it.

BARGE-WOMAN (*with a laugh*).   Pretty well, ma'am,
pretty well.

TOAD.   Ah !   (*He is gloomily silent*)

BARGE-WOMAN (*having finished with the horse*).   You
seem in trouble, ma'am.

TOAD.   Trouble !   Here's my married daughter she
sends off to me to come at once.   So off I comes, not
knowing what may be happening, but fearing the
worst, as you'll understand if you happen to be a
mother too, ma'am.   And I've left my business to
look after itself—I'm in the washing and laundering
line, as you can see, ma'am ; and I've left my breakfast, I was that upset, and I've lost all my money and
lost my way—and lost my breakfast, as you might
say, too, and as for my married daughter—well, you

G

know what it is, ma'am, being a married woman yourself, I dare say.

Barge-Woman. Dear, dear! Where might your married daughter be living?

Toad. Toad Hall, ma'am. The finest house in these parts, as no doubt you've heard tell. Tudor and Jacobean, my daughter tells me, with ornamental boathouse. That is, she lives just close to it.

Barge-Woman. Toad Hall? Why, I'm going that way myself. You come along in the barge with me, and I'll give you a lift.

Toad. I'm sure you're very kind, ma'am.

Barge-Woman. Don't mention it. So you're in the washing business. And a fine business you've got too, I dare say, if I'm not making too free in saying so.

Toad. Finest business in the whole country! All the gentry come to me! Washing, ironing, clear starching, making up gents' fine shirts for evening wear—all done under my own eye.

Barge-Woman. But surely you don't *do* it all yourself, ma'am?

Toad. Oh, I have girls, twenty or thirty of them always at work. But you know what girls are, ma'am. Idle trollops, that's what I call them.

Barge-Woman. They are that. And are you very fond of washing?

Toad. I love it. I simply dote on it. Never so happy as when I've got both arms in the wash-tub.

Barge-Woman. What a bit of luck meeting you!

Toad (*nervously*). Why, what do you mean?

Barge-Woman. Well, look at *me*. I like washing too, same as you. But there's my husband, who ought by rights to be here now, steering or looking after the horse, he has gone off with the dog to see if he can't pick up a rabbit for dinner somewhere. Says he'll catch us up at the next lock. Meantime, how am I to get on with my washing ?

TOAD. Oh, never mind about the washing. Try and fix your mind on that rabbit. Got any onions ?

BARGE-WOMAN. It's no good, I keep thinking of that washing. And if it's a pleasure to you to do it, as you say, being that fond of it, why then——

TOAD (*hastily*). No, no, I mustn't deprive you, not after you've been looking forward to it for weeks, as I expect you have. I'll steer, and then *you* can get on with your washing in your own way. The fact is, I am more used to gentlemen's things myself, shirt-fronts and cuffs—dressy things, if you know what I mean. It's my special line.

BARGE-WOMAN. I dare say the other would come just as easy to you once you began. Besides, it takes some practice to steer a barge properly, when you've never done it before.

TOAD. Never done it before ? Why, ma'am, it's my own recreation—after wash hours. First thing I do, as soon as I can get away, is to go down to the canal for a bit of barge-steering. It's got hold of me, my friends say, almost like a disease. Fact is, it's always been in the family. My father owned twenty or thirty barges—big ones—never less than three horses pulling them—great big enormous ones——

BARGE-WOMAN (*with suspicion*). I don't believe you're a washerwoman at all.

TOAD (*indignantly*). Of course I'm a washer-woman ! Should I be likely to say I was a washer-woman, if I wasn't ? It isn't a thing you want to go about saying, if you aren't.   Why should I be wearing a washerwoman's clothes if I'm not a washerwoman ?

BARGE-WOMAN (*firmly*).   Well, if you ask me, ma'am, I should say it's all a piece of deceit.   I don't go for to say what you're doing it for, but what I do say is, that I won't have deceit on my barge.   And that's for you, ma'am.

[*She goes to untie the bag from the horse's head.*

TOAD (*with dignity*).   Oh, indeed, ma'am !

BARGE-WOMAN.   And I say this, ma'am, that if you have a daughter, which I dare say you haven't, I'm sorry for her, having a mother which practises deceit. (*She comes away with the bag.*)   And I'll wish you good morning, ma'am.   [*She goes out, nose in air.*

TOAD (*shouting after her*).   You common, low, fat barge-woman, don't you dare to talk to your betters like that.   Washerwoman, indeed !   I would have you know that I am the Toad, the Terror of the Country-side, the Scourge of Barge-women !   Keep your stupid little barge !   I prefer—riding ! (*He unfastens the tow-rope, jumps on the horse's back and gallops off.*) The Toad !   The Toad !

BARGE-WOMAN (*rushing after him*).   Help !   Help ! The notorious Toad !   Help !

[*The* POLICEMAN *and the others join in the pursuit.*

ALL.   The Toad !   The Toad !

ACT IV

SCENE I

Rat's House by the River

SCENE.—*Rat's river-side residence. In construction it is something like the cabin of a ship. Through the large port-holes at the back, the opposite bank of the river can be seen. . . . Rat is busy with a large heap of pistols, swords, and cudgels.*

At one of the port-holes the head of the TOAD, *still wearing his washerwoman's bonnet over one eye, appears suddenly.*

TOAD (*from outside*). Help! Help!

RAT (*thoughtfully listening*). Funny! That sounded like Toad's voice.

TOAD. Help!

RAT. Yes, if Toad had been anywhere but where he is, poor unfortunate animal, I should have said——
[*He comes into* TOAD'S *line of sight.*

TOAD. Help! Help!

RAT (*turning round*). It is! Toady! How*ever*——

TOAD. Give us a hand, Rat. I'm about done.

RAT (*excitedly*). Old Toad! (*He seizes hold of him.*) Well, this *is*—— What's the matter? No strength left? *I* know. But how*ever*——?

TOAD. You'll have to pull me in. I'm about done.

RAT. That's all right. Got one kick left in you ? Good ! Well, when I say, ' Kick ', kick, and I'll pull, and—— Now then, ready ?

TOAD (*faintly*). Yes.

RAT. Then—kick ! (TOAD *kicks*. RAT *pulls, and he tumbles in on the floor.*)   There !

TOAD (*gasping*). Oh ! . . . Oh ! . . . Oh !

RAT (*helping him up*). Come on the sofa a bit, won't you ?

TOAD (*faintly*). Thank you, dear Ratty, thank you.
                            [*He flops on to the sofa.*

RAT. Here, drink this. You're about done.
                            [*He hands* TOAD *a bottle.*

TOAD (*drinking*). Ah ! (*He drinks again.*) That's better. I shall soon be all right. A passing faintness.

RAT (*looking at him*). Poor old Toady ! And wet as wet. . . . And am I wrong, or *are* you disguised in parts as a washerwoman who has seen better days ?

TOAD (*complacently*). Aha !

RAT. That's more like you. Escaped, eh ? In disguise ?

TOAD (*more complacently*). Aha ! (*He begins to sit up and take notice.*)

RAT. That's much better. We'll soon have you all right.

TOAD. It takes a good deal to put me out, Ratty. Just a passing faintness which might happen to any one who had been through what *I've* been through.

RAT. You've been through a lot, I expect.

TOAD. My dear Ratty, the times I've been through since I saw you last, you simply can't think !

RAT. Yes. Well, when you've got those horrible things off, and cleaned yourself up a bit——

TOAD. The times ! Such trials, such sufferings, and all so nobly borne !

RAT. You'll find some dry clothes upstairs——

TOAD. Such escapes, such disguises, such subterfuges, and all so cleverly planned and carried out !

RAT. Quite so. Well——

TOAD. Been in prison—got out of it, of course ! Stole a horse—rode away on it. Humbugged everybody—made 'em do exactly as I wanted. Oh, I *am* a smart Toad, and no mistake. Now what do you think my very last exploit was ?

RAT (*severely*). I don't know, Toad. But seeing where it was I found you, and the state you were in, I should say that somebody had dropped you into the river, and then thrown mud at you. It isn't a thing to boast about, really it isn't, Toad.

TOAD. Pooh, that was nothing. I just happened to be—to be heading a pursuit—on my horse—right in front of everybody else, in my usual way—and accidentally, not noticing the river in the enthusiasm of the chase—and the horse stopping a moment or two before I did——

RAT (*warningly*). Toad !

TOAD. But I wasn't going to tell you about that. Now what do you think——

RAT (*taking him by the shoulders*). Toad !

TOAD. Here, hold on a moment. I just want to tell you——

RAT. Toad, will you go upstairs at once, and see if you can possibly make yourself look like a respectable animal again, for a more shabby, bedraggled, disreputable-looking object than you are now, I never set eyes on.

TOAD (*with dignity*). You can hardly realize, Ratty, to whom you are——

RAT. Now stop swaggering and arguing and be off. Badger and Mole will be in directly——

TOAD (*airily*). Oh, ah! Yes, of course, the Mole and the Badger. What's become of them, the dear fellows? I had forgotten all about them.

RAT (*gravely*). Well may you ask!

TOAD. Why, what——

RAT. You will hear in good time. Badger himself may prefer to break the news to you. Be off now, and prepare yourself—why, what's the matter?

TOAD (*who has wandered in front of a mirror and is regarding himself with horror*). Is this glass of yours all right?

RAT. Of course. Why?

TOAD. I hoped—— You see, it's the first time I—— You're quite right, Ratty. Nobody could carry off a costume like this. (*Meekly*) I'll go and change. (*He goes out.*)

> [RAT, *left alone, fetches duster, pan, and brush, and begins to clean up after* TOAD, *murmuring* ' Dear, dear! ' *to himself, and* ' Well, I never! ' *While he is so engaged* BADGER *and* MOLE *come in.*

RAT (*eagerly*). Hallo, here you are! I say, what do you think?

MOLE (*dropping into a chair*). Too tired to think, Ratty, and that's a fact.

RAT. Yes, but——

BADGER (*gruffly*). Nobody thinks nowadays. That's the trouble. Too much action, not enough thought.

> [*He stretches himself on the sofa.*

RAT. Yes, but——

MOLE (*to* RAT). He's a bit low, just now. We've had a hard day. He'll be all right directly.

RAT. Yes, but what do you think ? Toad's back.

MOLE (*jumping up*). Toad ! Back where ?

RAT. Here !

MOLE. Where ?

RAT (*with a jerk of the head*). Cleaning. You ought to have seen him, Mole. He'd have made you laugh.

BADGER (*with his eyes shut*). Unhappy animal !

MOLE. Escaped ?

RAT (*nodding*). 'M. So he says. But you know what Toad is.

BADGER. I knew his father. Ah me !

MOLE. Has he heard the news ?

RAT. Not yet. I said Badger would tell him.

MOLE. Old Toad ! . . . He's just in time. Badger thinks it will be to-night !

RAT (*eagerly*). Not really ?

MOLE. Yes. *He* says so.

RAT. I've been polishing up the pistols and cutlasses. They're all ready.

MOLE. Good. We shall want all we can——

BADGER (*solemnly rousing himself*). Rat !

RAT (*turning round*). Hallo !

BADGER. Did I hear you say that our young friend Toad had escaped from his noisome dungeon ?

RAT. Came in five minutes ago. In such a state.

BADGER. I would speak with him.

RAT. He's just having a wash.

BADGER (*severely*). This is no time for washing. We have work before us to-night. Hard fighting.

Washing can wait.   Where do you think *I* should have been if, at the crisis of my life, I had stopped to wash ? Where would my revered father have been, if he had put soap before strategy ?   Where would my belovéd grandfather——

MOLE (*loudly*).   Toady !

TOAD (*from outside*).   Hallo, Mole, old fellow !

BADGER.   Thank you, Mole.

[*He closes his eyes again.*

MOLE (*to* RAT).   I heard all about his belovéd grandfather this morning.   Most interesting.

[TOAD *comes in, almost his old self.*

TOAD (*cheerily*).   Hallo, you fellows !

MOLE (*delightedly*).   Toady !

BADGER (*solemnly rising*).   Welcome home, Toad ! Alas ! what am I saying ?   Home, indeed.   This is a poor home-coming.   Unhappy Toad !

[*He sinks on to the sofa again.*

MOLE.   Fancy having *you* back !   And to-day of all days !   To think that you have escaped from prison, you clever, intelligent Toad.

TOAD.   Clever ?   Oh, no !   I'm not clever, really. Badger doesn't think so.   Rat doesn't think so.   I've only broken out of the strongest prison in England, that's all.   And disguised myself, and gone about the country on my horse humbugging everybody, that's all.   Clever ?   Oh dear, no.

RAT.   Oh, Toady !

TOAD.   Well, I shall be strolling along to Toad Hall. One does get appreciated at home.   Mole, if you like to drop in to coffee one evening, and care to hear a few of my milder adventures——

MOLE (*sadly*).   Oh, Toady, and you haven't heard !

TOAD. Heard what ? Quick, don't spare me !
What haven't I heard ?

MOLE. The Stoats and the Weasels !

RAT. The Wild-Wooders !

MOLE. And how they've been and gone——

RAT. And taken Toad Hall——

MOLE. And been living there ever since——

RAT. Going on simply anyhow——

MOLE. Lying in bed half the day——

RAT. Breakfast at all hours——

MOLE. Eating your grub and drinking your
drink——

RAT. And making bad jokes about you, and
singing vulgar songs——

MOLE. About——   [*He hesitates.*

RAT. About——   [*He hesitates.*

MOLE. Well, about prisons and magistrates, and
policemen.

RAT. Horrid personal songs with no humour in
them.

MOLE. That's what's happened, Toad. And it's no
good pretending it hasn't.

RAT. And they're all telling everybody that they've
come to Toad Hall to stay for good.

TOAD. Oh, have they ! I'll jolly soon see about
that !

RAT. Yes, but how ?

TOAD (*doubtfully*). Well—well—well, what I shall
do——

RAT. Of course, what you *ought* to do——

MOLE. No, he oughtn't. Nothing of the sort.
What he ought to do is, he ought to——

TOAD. Well, I shan't do it, anyhow. I've been

ordered about quite enough. It's my house we're talking about, and I know exactly what to do, and I'll tell you. I'm going to——

BADGER. Be quiet, all of you ! (*They are silent.*) Toad !

TOAD (*meekly*). Yes, Badger ?

BADGER. When you got into trouble a short time ago, and brought disgrace upon your own name, and shame and sorrow upon your friends, I resolved that on your return from your enforced seclusion, I would take the first opportunity of pointing out to you the folly of your ways.

TOAD (*meekly*). Yes, Badger. Thank you, Badger.

BADGER. I even went so far as to jot down a few rough notes on the subject. Where are they, Rat ?

RAT (*handing him a sheet of paper*) Here you are.

BADGER. Thank you. (*Reading*) ' To make suet dumplings——'

RAT. It's the other side.

BADGER. Ah yes, here we are.

TOAD (*meekly*). I'd rather have the bit about the dumplings, if it's all the same to you.

BADGER (*reading*). ' (1) Conceit and its consequence. (2) Reverend Uncle, grief of. (3) Toad, whither tending ? ' (*He puts the paper down.*) But the moment for all this is past.

TOAD (*humbly*). Just as you like, Badger, old man.

BADGER. The moment is past, because it is obvious now to everybody here where your folly has brought you. Toad Hall is in the hands of your enemies. Sentries guard it day and night. Unhappy Toad.

TOAD (*bursting into tears*). Alas, alas ! Toad Hall, that desirable river-side residence, in the hands of toats and Weasels ! This is, indeed, the end of everything !   *[He rolls on to the sofa in his grief.*

BADGER. Not quite the end. I haven't said my last word yet. Now I'm going to tell you a great secret. We are too few to attack from the front, but here is an underground passage that leads from the River Bank right up into the middle of Toad Hall.

TOAD (*sitting up brightly*). Oh, nonsense, Badger ! I know every inch of Toad Hall inside and out. You've been listening to gossip, that's what you've been doing.

BADGER (*severely*). Right up into the middle of Toad Hall. When your father, who was a particular friend of mine, told me about it, he said, ' Don't tell my son. He means well,' he said, ' but he's very light and irresponsible in character,' he said, ' and simply cannot hold his tongue. If he's ever in a real fix,' he said, ' and it would be of use to him,' he said, ' you may tell him. But not before.' That's what he said, Toad. Knowing the sort of animal you were.

TOAD. Well, well, perhaps I am a bit of a talker. A popular fellow such as I am, my friends get round me, we chaff, we sparkle, we tell witty stories and somehow my tongue gets wagging. I have the gift of conversation. I have been told that I ought to have a *salon*, whatever that may be.

BADGER (*severely*). At present, my young friend, you haven't even got a box-room.

TOAD (*sweetly*). How true, dear Badger, and how well put. But you have a plan in that wise old head of yours. This passage. How shall we use it ?

BADGER. To-night the Chief Weasel is giving a banquet. It's his birthday. While they are all feasting, careless of the morrow, we four, armed to the teeth, will creep silently, by way of the passage, into the butler's pantry.

Toad. Ah ! that squeaky board in the butler's pantry !

Badger. Armed to the teeth, you and Rat, by one door——

Rat (*looking up*). Yes, Badger.

Badger. And me and Mole by the other——

Mole. Yes, Badger.

Badger. Also armed to the teeth—we shall——

Mole. Creep out of the pantry——

Rat. With our pistols, and swords, and sticks——

Badger. And rush in on them——

Toad (*ecstatically*). And whack 'em and whack 'em and whack 'em.

Badger. Exactly. (*He pats* Toad *on the back.*) You have caught the spirit of it perfectly. Good Toad !

Toad. I'll learn 'em to steal my house.

Rat. Teach 'em, Toad, not learn 'em.

Badger. But we don't *want* to teach 'em. Toad's quite right. We want to *learn* 'em, and, what's more, we're going to. Now then, to rest, all of you. We start at 9 o'clock, and we must be fresh for it.

[*He settles down on the sofa.*

Rat. I'll just get the lanterns trimmed.

[*He goes out.*

Mole (*settling down in a chair*). Badger's right. I want a rest.

Toad (*drawing a chair next to* Mole). Yes, we must rest.

[*He begins to chuckle.* Mole, *eyes closed, takes*

no notice. TOAD *glances at him and chuckles*
more loudly. MOLE *lazily opens an eye.*

MOLE (*sleepily*).   Eh ?

TOAD (*laughing heartily*).   I was just thinking—
most amusing thing—really rather funny—I was in a
hollow tree—and a policeman—well, a whole army of
'em, was looking for me—and one of 'em said, ' Is that
a bird ? '—ha, ha, ha !—really very funny—' Is that a
bird or what ? '—and what do you think *I* did ?—ha,
ha, ha !—I said——   [*And so on.* MOLE *sleeps.*

SCENE 2

The Underground Passage

SCENE.—*The Secret Passage. The four conspirators steal in*—BADGER, RAT, MOLE, TOAD. BADGER *and* MOLE *carry the lanterns. They are all armed to the teeth.*

BADGER (*to* RAT).   H'sh !
RAT (*to* MOLE).   H'sh !
MOLE (*to* TOAD).   H'sh !
TOAD (*loudly*).   *What ?*
THE OTHERS.   H'sh !
TOAD.   Oh, all right.
BADGER.   We are now in the secret passage, but not yet under the house. For the moment silence is not absolutely necessary, but later on——

TOAD (*airily*).   Quite so, quite so !

BADGER.   Now, it's all understood ?   Mole and I burst into the banqueting hall by the east door, and drive them towards the west door, where Rat and Toad——

TOAD (*impatiently*).   That's all right, Badger. Let's get at 'em.

BADGER.   Rat, you're responsible for the operations on the western front.   You understand ? . . . What's the matter ?

RAT (*who is trying to read something by the light of* MOLE'S *lantern*).   Just before we start, hadn't we better make sure we've got everything ?   (*Reading*) One belt, one sword, one cutlass, one cudgel, one pair pistols, one policeman's truncheon, one policeman's whistle——   [TOAD *blows his loudly.*

BADGER (*alarmed*). What's that?

MOLE (*reproachfully*). Toad!

BADGER (*sternly*). Was that you, Toad?

TOAD (*meekly*). I just wanted to be sure it worked.

BADGER. Now, Toad, I warn you solemnly, if I have any trouble from *you*, you'll be sent back, as sure as fate.

TOAD (*humbly*). Oh, Badger!

BADGER. Well, I warn you.

RAT. One policeman's whistle, two pairs of hand-cuffs, bandages, sticking-plaster, flask, sandwich-case. Now, has everybody got that?

BADGER (*with a laugh*). I've got it, but I'm going to do all I want to do with this here stick.

RAT. It's just as you like, Badger. It's only that I don't want you to blame me afterwards and say that I'd forgotten anything.

BADGER. Well, well! But no pistols, unless we have to. We shall only be shooting each other.

RAT. Pistols in reserve, of course. Eh, Moly?

MOLE. Of course. Eh, Toad?

TOAD (*who is examining his*). Of course.

[*It goes off with a tremendous bang. Everybody jumps.*

MOLE (*reproachfully*). Toad!

BADGER. Toad? You don't mean to say that that was Toad again? After what I've just said?

TOAD. I—I just—I didn't——

BADGER. Very well then, you go back.

TOAD (*falling on his knees*). Oh, please, Badger, please!

BADGER. No! I can't take the risk.

TOAD. Oh, Badger, please. After all I've been

H

through—and my own house too. You *mustn't* send me back.

BADGER (*wavering*). I ought to.

MOLE. Look here, I'll go last and keep an eye on him——

RAT. And we'll take his pistols and his whistle away. (*He does so.*)

BADGER. Well——

RAT. We'll leave 'em here, see. (*He puts them on the ground.*) Just here. It might be very useful, if we had to beat a retreat, to find a couple of freshly primed pistols and a policeman's whistle to fall back on. That'll be all right, Badger.

BADGER (*gruffly*). Very well. (*He leads on.*) Now then, no more talking. From this moment absolute silence.

TOAD (*very humbly*). Just before we begin the silence, Badger——

BADGER (*after waiting in silence*). Well, what is it?

TOAD. A-a-a-a—tishoo! That's all. I felt it coming. Now I won't say another word.

[*They pass on*

SCENE 3

The Banqueting-room in Toad Hall

SCENE.—*The banqueting-room—a magnificent apartment —in Toad Hall. It being the* CHIEF WEASEL'S *birthday, a banquet is in progress. The hero of the occasion, a laurel-wreath on his brow, sits at the head of the main table, his admirers round him. Pressed for a few more words, he rises.*

CHIEF WEASEL. Friends and Fellow Animals. Before we part this evening I have one final toast to propose. (*Hear, hear!*) It is a toast which on all occasions has something of solemnity in it, something even of sadness, but never more so than on this occasion. 'Absent Friends.' (*Hear, hear!*) Absent Friends. With this toast I couple first the name of our kind host, Mr. Toad. (*Loud laughter.*) Although unable to be present himself to-night—(*laughter*)— owing to a previous engagement—(*laughter*)—Mr. Toad has generously put his entire establishment at our disposal for as long as we like to make use of it. (*Loud laughter.*) We all know Toad—(*hear, hear!*)—good Toad, wise Toad, modest Toad. (*Laughter.*) It is a personal sorrow to every one of us that he is not amongst us to-night. Let me sing you a little song which I have composed on this subject. (*Hear, hear!*)

> Toad he went a pleasuring
> 　Gaily down the road—
> They put him in prison for twenty years :
> 　　Poor —old —Toad !

Toad he had a beautiful house,
A most refined abode—
They put him in prison for twenty years :
    Poor—old—Toad !

Toad he had much money and goods
All carefully bestowed—
They put him in prison for twenty years :
    Poor—old—Toad !

Chief Weasel. Chorus, please.

    Poor—old—Toad !
    Poor—old—Toad !
    They put him in prison for twenty years :
    Poor—old—Toad !

[Loud applause.

Chief Weasel. But while we are thinking of our good host, Mr. Toad, we must not forget our other absent friends—Mr. Badger, Mr. Rat and Mr. Mole. (*Laughter.*) It is a particular sorrow to me that they are not with us to-night, living as they do—unlike Mr. Toad—so very conveniently in the neighbourhood. From time to time, indeed, of late, we have caught glimpses of them—behind hedges. (*Laughter.*) We have seen their back views—(*laughter*)—in the distance —(*laughter*)—running away. (*Laughter.*) We know that they cannot plead absence from the country as an excuse for their absence from our board, so that the only reason for it must be excessive shyness. (*Laughter.*) Modesty. (*Laughter.*) All the more do we regret that they did not see fit to join us. Fellow animals, I give you the toast—' Absent Friends ! '

ALL (*rising and drinking*).   Absent Friends !

A DEEP VOICE OUTSIDE.   Absent Friends !

ALL (*to each other*).   What's that ? . . . What is it ? . . . I didn't hear anything. . . . Nonsense. . . .

> [*The door opens.* BADGER *and* MOLE *rush in.*

BADGER (*his war-cry*).   Up the Badger !

MOLE (*his*).   A Mole !   A Mole !

BADGER (*wielding his cudgel*).   Lay on to 'em, boys.

MOLE (*between blows*).   Sorry we're late, Weasel—(*biff !*)—but many thanks all the same—(*biff !*)—for the kind invitation.   (*Biff !*)

CHIEF WEASEL.   The other door !   Quick !

> [*The other door opens, and* TOAD *and* RAT *charge*
> *in.*

TOAD (*terribly*).   I've come home, Weasel.   (*He makes for him.*)   How are *you* ?   (*Bang !*)   Toad he went a-pleasuring, did he !   (*Bang !*)   I'll pleasure you !   (*Bang !*)

THE ENEMY (*variously*).   Help ! . . . Mercy ! . . . All *right*, all right ! . . . I say, *shut* up !

BADGER.   Wallop 'em, boys.   Keep walloping !

> [*Some of the enemy are showing fight, some are*
> *escaping through the doors and windows, some*
> *are begging for mercy with uplifted paws.*

RAT (*to one of the weaker brethren*).   Surrender, do you ?   All right.   Get in that corner there.

> [*There is a small rush for ' that corner there'.*

MOLE (*seeking whom he can devour*).   A Mole !   A Mole !   (*To an unhappy Stoat.*)   Hallo, were *you* looking for anything ?   (*Biff !*)   Just wanted to say good-bye ?   (*Biff !*)   *Good*-bye !   (*Biff !*)   Sorry you can't stop.   [*He biffs him out of the door.*

TOAD (*to a terrified Ferret*). Good evening! Do you sing at all?

FERRET. N-no, sir, please, sir.

TOAD. Not just a *little* song?

FERRET. N-no, sir. I—I never l-learnt singing.

TOAD (*swinging his club*). Not just a *funny* little song about a poor old Toad?

FERRET (*with an effort*). N-no, sir.

TOAD (*ingratiatingly*). Try!

FERRET (*foolishly—in a high squeaky voice*). Poor—old—Toad!

TOAD (*furiously*). I'll learn you to sing!

   [*With a squeal the Ferret scurries into* RAT'S *corner*.

RAT (*getting in front of* TOAD). All prisoners here, Toad. I'm looking after them.

     [*He walks up and down in front of them, pistol in hand*.

BADGER (*walloping the last of the others out of the window*). There! That's the lot! (*He wipes his brow*). A pity! I was just beginning to enjoy it. What about your little party, Rat?

RAT. They've surrendered. I thought they might come in useful, waiting on us and so on.

BADGER. If any of 'em *wants* to go on for a bit longer——

CHORUS. No, sir, please, sir.

BADGER. Ah!

     [*He looks round the room.* TOAD *is conducting an imaginary battle with a particularly stubborn adversary*.

TOAD (*getting his blow in*). Aha! (*Dodging an imaginary one*) That's no good. (*Getting another in*) More like *that*! . . .

BADGER.   Hallo ! (TOAD, *recalled to himself, breaks
off the engagement rather sheepishly.*)   Now then, Toad,
stir your stumps, and look lively.   I want some grub,
I do.   We've got your house back for you, and you
don't offer us so much as a sandwich.

RAT.   Just a moment, Badger.   What about the
sentries ?

BADGER.   Sentries, yes.

RAT.   They may be still at their posts.

TOAD.   Sentries, pooh !   They've run away far
enough by now, haven't they, Mole ?

MOLE.   If they're wise they have.

RAT.   I think it would be safer if Mole and I just——

BADGER.   Sensible Rat.   There spoke the voice of
wisdom.   (*Picking up his cudgel*) You and I and
Mole——

RAT.   Don't you bother, Badger.   Mole and I——

BADGER (*grimly*).   When I go walloping I *go*
walloping.

TOAD.   So do I.   Come on, I'll lead the way.

BADGER.   You will do nothing of the sort, Toad.
You've asked us to stay to supper and we're staying
to supper.   Well, where is the supper ?   If this isn't
your house, say so, and Mole can entertain us.

RAT (*indicating the prisoners*).   They'll help you get
it ready, Toady.

TOAD (*reluctantly*).   Oh, all right.

MOLE (*to* TOAD, *as the others go out*).   Don't forget
the wine, Toad.   We shall want to drink your health,
and you'll have to make a speech.

TOAD (*cheering up*).   Oh, right, right.   That's all
right, leave that to me.

     [MOLE *goes out*. TOAD *is left with the now*

*penitent prisoners—about eight of the smaller
Stoats and Ferrets.*

TOAD (*to his slaves*).   Now then, bustle up !

[*They bustle up eagerly.*

CHORUS.   Yes, sir, coming, sir !

TOAD.   Get busy.

CHORUS.   Yes, sir, please, sir !

TOAD.   I owe you a leathering apiece, as it is.

CHORUS.   Please, sir, no, sir !

TOAD.   Well, get busy, and perhaps I won't say
any more about it.

[*They are very busy and the hall begins to look
tidy again.*

TOAD (*sitting down at the head of the table*).   Got a
pencil, any of you ?

ONE OF THEM.   Yes, sir.

TOAD (*taking it*).   Thanks. . . . All right, don't
hang about, get busy.

[*He takes a piece of paper from his pocket and
begins to write.*

THE PRISONERS (*whispering to each other*).   He's
writing. . . . He's writing a letter. . . . It isn't a
letter. . . . It's *my* pencil he's using. . . . I wonder
who he's writing to. . . . Shall we ask him what he's
writing ?. . . I will if you will. . . . *You* ask him,
it's your pencil. . . . No, you . . . all right, I don't
mind. . . . Well, go on then.

THE BRAVE ONE.   Please, sir——

TOAD (*proudly*).   There !

THE BRAVE ONE.   Please, sir——

TOAD.   Now, I dare say all you young fellows are
wondering what I've been doing ?

CHORUS.   Please, sir, yes, sir.

TOAD. Well, I've just been jotting down a few rough notes.

CHORUS. Oo, sir.

TOAD. Just a few notes for a little entertainment I have sketched out—a little informal singsong or conversazione to celebrate my return.

CHORUS. Yes, sir, thank you, sir.

TOAD. Something like this——

(1) Speech—By Toad.

And then I make a note. 'There will be other speeches by Toad during the evening.' Just so as to reassure people.

CHORUS. Yes, sir.

TOAD. (2) Address—By Toad.

Synopsis—you all know what that means, of course ?

CHORUS. Please, sir, no, sir.

TOAD. Well, it just means—well, you'll see what it means directly. It's just a sort of synopsis.

CHORUS. Yes, sir.

TOAD. Synopsis. Our Prison System—The Art of Disguise—Barge Life—Steeple-chasing and its dangers—A Typical English Squire.

CHORUS. Yes, sir.

TOAD. (3) Imitations of Various Bird Notes. By Toad.

(4) Song—By Toad. (Composed by Himself.)

(5) Other compositions by Toad. (Sung by the Composer.)

(6) Song. 'For He's a Jolly Good Fellow.' (Sung by Badger, Rat, and Mole.)

CHORUS. Oo, sir.

TOAD. That's all, just a few rough notes. Of

course it may shape a little differently as the evening
goes on.   There are one or two conjuring tricks which
I used to know—something to do with three billiard
balls and a globe of goldfish—they may come back to
me or they may not.   We shall see.

CHORUS. Yes, sir, thank you, sir.

THE BRAVE ONE. Could you give us the song
now, sir ?

TOAD (*pleased*).   Give it you now, eh ?

CHORUS. Oo, please, sir.

TOAD. Well, well.

    [*He gets up and walks to the middle of the room.*

THE BRAVE ONE (*picking up the* CHIEF WEASEL'S
wreath). Wouldn't you like to wear this, sir ?

TOAD. You think—eh ?—— Well, perhaps you're
right.   [*He puts it on.*

CHORUS. Oo, *sir* !

TOAD. Suits me, eh ?

CHORUS. Please, sir, yes, sir.

TOAD. Some people can wear 'em and some can't.
You have the manner or you haven't. There it is.
You can't explain it.

CHORUS. Yes, sir. Where will you stand, sir ?

THE BRAVE ONE (*bringing a stool*). Won't you
stand on this, sir ?

TOAD (*modestly mounting*). Well, perhaps——

CHORUS. Oo, *sir* !

TOAD. Now this is just a *little* song, and it's called
' When the Toad came Home.'

CHORUS. Yes, sir.

TOAD. There's only one verse at present, but it
can be sung any number of times.

THE BRAVE ONE. Yes, sir. May we all sing it ?

TOAD. Certainly, certainly. It is really composed
with the idea of being sung by a great many people.

CHORUS. Yes, sir.

> [*They group themselves round him, expectantly.*

TOAD (*solemnly*). ' When the Toad came Home.'

> [*Singing.*

The Toad—came—home !

There was panic in the parlour, there was howling in
the hall,

There was crying in the cow-shed and a snorting in
the stall,

There was smashing in of window, there was crashing
in of door,

There was bashing of the enemy who fainted on
the floor,

When the Toad—came—home !

> [*All the prisoners dance in a circle round* TOAD,
> *singing this song.* TOAD *stands wreathed above
> them, raptly enjoying it. In the middle of
> the second verse* BADGER, RAT *and* MOLE
> *return.*

BADGER (*appalled*). Toad ! Get down at once !

> [TOAD *does not hear him. He is far away. The
> singers finish their verse, but go on dancing
> round the hero.*

MOLE (*reproachfully*). Toady !

RAT (*to* BADGER). It's no good. I know him.
He's practically in a trance.   Let him have his evening
out.

MOLE. We'll talk to him in the morning.

RAT. Talking's no good to Toad. He'll always
come back to what he is.

BADGER (*grimly*).   All the same, I'll talk to him.

RAT.   But let him have his hour first.

BADGER.   Oh, all right.

> [*They stand watching. The dancers are singing again now. . . .*

MOLE (*apologetically*).   You know, there's something about that tune. . . . It's only just . . . I shan't be . . .

> [*And suddenly he is in the circle, dancing and singing.*

BADGER.   He's very young still, is Mole.

RAT.   Y-yes.

BADGER.   The best of fellows, of course. But young, young.

RAT.   Y-yes. . . . All the same, I don't see why . . . I mean, after all . . . I . . . well, I . . . Excuse me l   [*And now he, too, is in the circle.*

> [*But others seem to have heard the news. The Jury come on, singing and dancing——*

JURY.

> There were calls from all the neighbours,
>   there were letters from afar—

> —*followed by the* JUDGE *and the* USHER.

JUDGE.

> There was groaning on the Bench—

USHER.

> —and there was moaning at the Bar.

> *Then* PHOEBE—

PHOEBE.

> There was tooting on the piccolo and fluting on
>   the pipes.

> —*and the* WASHERWOMAN *and* BARGE-WOMAN.

WOMEN.

There was starching of 'is sockses and a washing
of 'is wipes,

ALL.

When the Toad came home, When the Toad
came home.

Enter ALFRED.

ALFRED.

There was shrieking in the gear-box, there was
trumpeting of horn,

And the elephant was jealous and the parrot felt
forlorn.

ALL.

There were speeches from the gentry, there was
moistening of throats,

Enter POLICEMAN.

POLICEMAN.

And a moistening of pencils and a taking down
of notes.

ALL.

When the Toad came home, When the Toad came
home.

[*Now they are all round* TOAD, *singing and
dancing ; all but* BADGER.

BADGER.   Well, well, well !   (*Doubtfully*) Well——
(*Less doubtfully*) W-w-well ?   (*His mind made up*) Oh,
well !

[*He joins the dancers, and hobbles stiffly round
with them.*

ALL.

There was welcoming to Badger, when he joined
the merry throng.

BADGER.

I can do it for a little but I can't go on for long. . . .
        [*And so on. The incense of their adoration
        streams up to the be-laureiled* TOAD, *and with
        a long sigh of happiness he closes his eyes.*

EPILOGUE

The Wind in the Willows

It is Spring again. The wind is whispering in the willows that fringe the river. Faintly we hear its elfin music. Among her daffodils lies MARIGOLD, *in tumbled sleep. The dead leaves in the hollow rise and fall ; they fall apart as an old grey* BADGER *heaves himself into the sunlight. Curiously he sniffs at* MARIGOLD, *and then lumbers away. A* WATER-RAT *twinkles out of his hole in the bank ; a* MOLE *laboriously takes the air ; they, too, pass the time of day with* MARIGOLD *before following in the wake of the* BADGER. *Last of all comes a* TOAD. '* Ah, Marigold, Marigold ! '*—and so, waddling jauntily, after the others. . . .*
But NURSE *is getting impatient. From afar her voice comes to us.*

NURSE. Marigold ! Marigold ! It's time we went, dear !

> [MARIGOLD *sighs gently, and stirs a little in her sleep.*